Pocket Venus

Pocket Venus

THE RISE, FALL & RISE OF A HOLLYWOOD STARLET

AUSTIN MUTTI-MEWSE

First published in 2018 by Zuleika,
89G Lexham Gardens, London, W8 6JN

Designed by Euan Monaghan
Printed and bound in Great Britain by
Marston Book Services Ltd, Oxfordshire

A CIP record for this book
is available from the British Library
ISBN 978-1-9996232-2-7

In Memory of Mildred 'Cissie' Shay

For Joanna, Nathan & Howard

One

Departures and Arrivals

October 2005

I lay on my side and watched the California sunshine creep across the parquet floor to the mattress I had been sleeping on. I felt as if I hadn't had much sleep. I was woken early by the caws of tropical birds kept in cages plonked on the dining table, atop the sideboard, and even on the floor of the dining room next door. I looked up at the ceiling. My journey here was coming to an end.

Mildred had needed me twice in the night and had called for me from her narrow bed in a single room across the hall. She'd finally settled down at three in the morning. The birds had started squawking soon after.

I peeled back the thin sheet and rolled stiffly onto the hardwood floor. This was the largest room in the property. I sat down on a sofa; its material, once red, was now bleached almost white by the sun. The room still displayed the signs of having once been grand, with elegant woodwork and a fabulous fireplace. Now the fireplace was still remarkable, but for different reasons: it was covered with an unimaginable rainbow paintwork effect that spread to the surrounding walls and the floor.

This was the handiwork of Mildred's fifty-something year old daughter, Baby.

The house, in the smart hillside district of Glendale, California, had once belonged to Mildred's late sister Adeline Shay; it was now very much Baby's. I looked at my watch: seven o'clock. Baby was nowhere to be seen. I pulled on shorts over my boxers, and a T-shirt and flip-flops from where I had left them folded on the floor next to the mattress. The shorts were covered in dog hair. I brushed them down.

The birds were settled. The house was silent. I decided to see if Mildred had woken up, and tip-toed across the hall. I opened her bedroom door and found her sitting on the side of her bed in a 1950s blue floral bathing costume and bed socks. Her hair was dyed blonde, and her bed-head was wild.

Mildred's eyes told me she was happy to see me, despite one side of her smile drooping downwards. She gestured to me to join her on the bed. She took my hand in hers as I approached. With her other hand, she reached for her prayer book on the side-table. Underneath it was her scrapbook from her days as Mildred Shay, the movie star. The cover photos that were staring up at me were of Mildred with Alan Ladd, Mildred with Cary Grant. The corners were curled, the book well-thumbed.

Mildred pulled away an elastic band from her prayer book. A photo of an infant Baby in her father Geoffrey's arms, and a second of Mildred with Errol Flynn, fell to the floor. As I retrieved them, Mildred opened the book at a marked page. Her index finger traced the words of a prayer – a prayer for the traveller. I nudged closer and placed my arm around her. I could hear her whispering but her words were indecipherable. Her dribble was wetting the page. I wiped it away with a tissue from my shorts pocket. She turned to me with a hint of a smile, and then back to the page. I joined her in reading the words aloud:

You already know the destination, Lord, and the chal-
lenges I face. So I pray that Your Army of Angels will
go before me and make every crooked path straight…

Later that morning, I stood with my wheelie-case on the sloping driveway. A blue taxi was waiting on the winding street above. When we had said our goodbyes in the house, Mildred had become upset, adamant that it wouldn't be our last time together. I knew it would. Baby stood on the driveway with me; her long legs in short-shorts. Her former pop-star husband, Gordon Waller, was speaking with the driver. I turned around. To my surprise, I saw Mildred propping herself up in the doorway. She was still in the blue bathing suit, now topped off with a giant sun-hat. She was waving and trying to speak, but the words were again unclear. I left the case and returned to her side. The strength of her embrace, despite the stroke and the effects of the brain tumour, told that me that she knew that we wouldn't meet again. As I pulled away she stared up at me. She had applied lipstick. She focused. Her words, for the first time in four days, were quite audible.

'See you around, kid.'

Two years earlier

The Cundy Street flats in London, three symmetrical Art Deco-style blocks, each neatly manicured, were the kind of dwellings people stared at from the top deck of a bus, it was a window into another world: the inhabitants were a mishmash of aristocracy, former MPs, and erstwhile trailblazers. In the gloom of the winter day, lamplight flickered from the large windows: curtain up, showtime.

I stood in the car park next to my rusty, red VW Gold, facing onto Ebury Street. Across the way a blue plaque shone with one single name that surely transcended any celebrity now residing there: Mozart. My fiancée, Joanna, remained in the car, sitting in the passenger seat, on her mobile to her mother. Joanna's legs were straddling a battered cool-box; her mood like its contents: chilly at best. Safe to say we weren't really talking.

I left her, grabbed a small grey hold-all and a flowered shopper from the car boot, and walked to the entrance of Kylestrome House. Inside the atmosphere was stark, with no signs of life. An almost Victorian-era wheelchair contraption was parked up outside Flat 1. The curved walls were painted a cold blue. By the time I reached the fourth floor I was puffing. I scrambled in my pocket for the door key – Flat 18. There was a click and the door opened, slowly at first as it wrestled with a stubborn doormat on the other side.

I was apprehensive. I'd known Mildred Shay six months, and now I was moving in. A month previously I had asked Mildred if we could stay for a couple of weeks. She had been delighted at the thought. A deal had been struck: we would buy all the food and cook for her – Joanna, mostly. This had pleased Mildred immensely. Mildred was no cook. She had told me how she was living on ready-meals ('crap in cardboard', she had called them) delivered from the convenience store run by 'that nice Arabian' Mr Ali on the corner of Ebury Street. It was a win-win situation, considering that my and Joanna's current financial status verged on broke. I was a freelance obituary writer at *The Daily Telegraph*, but the life had gone out of death. My subjects, Old Hollywood film stars, weren't dying off quickly enough, and with payment on death, Mildred's offer couldn't have come at a better time. Besides, I'd promised Joanna it was only temporary.

Mildred was less thrilled about Joanna, though. She had referred to her as 'the other woman' in a jokey way – maybe? Mildred had met Joanna and they had got on *okay*. The simple fact was that both were opinionated, and Mildred preferred men. And she liked me, a lot.

I dropped the bags and pulled the front door shut behind me, my hands clammy. The flat was hot. I was struck by a smell, the very same as I had smelt before on my first visit: a sickly odour of sweet perfume, mixed with that sticky aroma of hairspray, and then cat – moreover, cat pee. My stomach turned. I recognised the perfume as Giorgio Beverly Hills, a metonym for film stars, sunshine, and glamour.

Before me was a long hall with a threadbare carpet underfoot and yellowing painted doors on either side. Single bulbs hung in basic cotton shades – the light was dim. All the doors were shut tight. The smell of deterioration triggered a memory: when I was a young boy at the Horniman Museum in London. I could remember being dwarfed by stuffed animals, disturbed by the hundreds of dead birds of paradise perched motionless on twigs encased behind dusty glass. I recalled an overwhelming feeling of pity for those once-colourful creatures, with only a glimmer of their past glories visible in their clipped and faded wings.

The walls were cluttered. Mismatched picture frames contained faded photographs of film stars who peered out at me. I recognised Mildred with Katharine Hepburn; Mildred with Roy Rogers and his trusty steed Trigger; Mildred with Marilyn Monroe and Sammy Davis Jnr.; Mildred arm-in-arm with Nelson Eddy, her Max Factor smile covered by pitted glass.

A flickering light seeped out from under the door at the far end of the hall. From the other side came a frantic scratching. It suddenly stopped dead. Despite the dilapidated surroundings, I knew the glamour hadn't left completely, for in that room, behind that door, resided a movie star.

I pushed it open. Suddenly the very walls seemed to shake. I was deafened by the ridiculously high volume of a TV set at the far end of the living room; it was so loud that everything about me trembled. Fine china and crystal on the shelves beside me danced, then collided with the vigorousness of the vibration. Mildred hadn't noticed me, but her cat Rosebud had. Rosebud hissed wildly, the bottom of the door indented with her deep scratches.

Mildred was sitting in the epicentre, tilted back in

a leatherette recliner, wiggling her feet. Her long toe-nails, painted Jungle Red, were sticking like claws through the fronts of high-heeled rattan straw wedges. She was dressed like a teenager, in shiny Lycra leggings and a jacket of a similar material with baseball emblems on the arm and the remnants of a meal down the front. She wore the collars up; a dozen rows of multi-coloured beads were slung around her neck, off-set with large pink plastic earrings. The entire get-up was reminiscent of Sandy colliding with Frenchie from the film *Grease*.

'Hi, Mildred,' I bellowed.

'Oh, darling?' she said, slightly startled; her smile was wide, her eyes energetic. 'Oh, Gawd, I'd forgotten you were coming today. Why, I'd have dressed up for you. I'm a wreck.' But her look was so considered that I wondered if she wasn't just toying with me.

'I let myself in with your spare key,' I shouted, waving it at her.

She reached for a lipstick from a side table next to her, and, as she applied it blindly, she pointed at the TV and shouted, 'Listen, that's my favourite TV show, darling. See her? I knew that Angela Lansbury woman when we were together at Metro-Goldwyn-Mayer.'

I glanced at the TV and back at Mildred. 'Wait a minute,' she yelled as she fumbled for the TV remote, muting Angela.

'Oh, that's better,' she smiled. 'Listen, is your girl-friend here too?' she asked, trying to peer round me into the hall.

'Yes – well, no, Joanna is still down by the car, un-loading the rest of our luggage.'

'She is! Oh, Gawd, you mean we haven't even one night together before 'the wife' arrives?' She roared with laughter. 'Oh, that's fine, darling…You've got the big bedroom, the one I showed you before. I've unlocked it and moved out all my raunchy sex stuff.' She winked and giggled and then stared back at the TV.

'Oh, I've gotta watch my show: *Murder, She Wrote*. That actress Kathryn Grayson is in this week's episode and Oh, Gawd, she's gotten so darn fat! I mean, Kathryn Grayson used to be so thin in those Howard Keel musicals. You gotta see how fat she has got!' Her hands were wide apart, illustrating the width of her old friend. 'I mean, she was such a star at MGM. I can't understand it, when we were under contract at the studios I ate lettuce with a squirt of lemon juice and a mouthful of diet pills for lunch, and it wasn't really all that long ago. Was it?'

She stopped talking for a heartbeat and grabbed the remote, pointed it towards the TV, and pressed the un-mute button. This triggered the vibrations again.

I left Mildred hunched forward in the chair, gazing open-mouthed at the TV.

As I turned to leave, she called after me, 'Oh, Orstin, you've just gotta see the size of her arse. I mean, what can she be putting into that mouth?!'

'Later, I'll watch later,' I shouted as I began to pull the door behind me. Rosebud leapt from the hall, through my legs, and onto Mildred's lap. The cat turned, hissed, and clawed the air with great disapproval.

I entered the bedroom and tossed the bags onto the bed. The room was silent, undisturbed, with an incongruous mix of furniture: a double divan, a to-mato-red painted chest of drawers, and a tall Art Deco-style chest against faded fawn-coloured walls. The carpet, a feeble shade of turquoise, had had huge swathes eaten away in places by moths, revealing a wooden herringbone floor underneath. By the window, broken curtain hooks looked like fragments of bone. There was a feeling of abandonment: the moths had been allowed free range. I walked across to the large sash window. The white paintwork was spotted with glistening black mould. The glass pane showed signs of activity, as with closer inspection I noticed faint finger-prints on it – someone had been looking out, but not recently.

I spied Joanna down below in a parking space. Her head was obstructed from full view by the open boot of my car and an overhanging cyanosis shrub. I watched as her head emerged from the boot. She straightened up, turned, and spied me. I waved, but she didn't reciprocate.

I left the flat's front door ajar as I quickly headed down the four flights of stairs. Taking two steps at a time, I was soon in the entrance hall. I went out of the main front door to where I'd seen Joanna. Now in the driver's seat, Joanna was staring at her mobile phone. She wound down the window.

'Hi, Joanie, she's ready for us – well, sort of,' I said, trying to be upbeat.

'Well, thank God, what have you been doing? You've been ages.' She looked back at her phone. 'I've been on the phone to Mum for twenty minutes!'

'That's an exaggeration, Joanie – more like ten.'

'Oh, look, I need a hand,' she said. Her accent still had a hint of home: the Forest of Dean, Gloucestershire. She pointed at the cool-box: 'There's the fridge stuff too.'

I noticed Joanna's apprehension: she always called her mum when she was agitated. Her tone was sharper than it had been on our way here; her frown lines were deeper. I opened the door. She got out and we both grabbed more of our luggage from the back seat.

The car was now empty; everything else that we had taken from our old flat last week was now with friends, or with Joanna's mum and dad in the Forest of Dean. They'd stored our furniture too, in one of their sheds. I prayed it was watertight – most of our stuff was Ikea chipboard. I'd left even more possessions (lamps, CDs, china, and books) in cardboard boxes at my parents' house in Worthing. My mother was less than happy about me filling up their half-empty loft. It felt odd to have the only evidence of our relationship in two bin liners, a dozen bags, and a wheelie-case.

After what seemed like forever, Joanna followed me to the flat. Our hands full, she pushed the front door open with her elbow. Suddenly the living room door flew open and, as if she'd been waiting for the curtain to rise, there was Mildred, bejewelled hands outstretched, diamond bracelets running the length of her arms, and in a change of costume: a batwing cocktail dress with sling-backs over fishnets. She had back-combed her hair too – it was now the size of a spaceman's helmet. Like a yellow lollypop and just as sticky, it had a matted appearance thanks to lashings of lacquer. The make-up was pan-stick, her false eye-lashes peeling away slightly at the corners. The cyclamen lipstick was painted over and above the lip-line, Marlene Dietrich-style. The eyebrows were arched in the same way Jean Harlow wore hers shortly after her own arrival in Hollywood – seductive and high.

Squealing like a teenager, her greeting was dramatic; the contents of a can of soda in her hand flicked over the hall walls. But the glumness of the hall was lifted by her presence. Joanna, although speechless, was at least smiling. It was impossible not to. Mildred's manifestation was akin to a pantomime dame.

'Come in, darlings, come in! You know what, kids, I haven't had roomies since 1932 when I shacked up with Ginger Rogers and Betty Grable at the Garden of Allah on Sunset Boulevard.'

Mildred clip-clopped towards us and stood partially blocking the entrance to the bedroom. 'Ginger and I would run naked through the grounds and head to the spa for a massage!' Mildred looked at me saucily. 'Now that was something to see! Ginger was real slim back then, and gorgeous, with long golden hair...' she said, pulling at her dress to accentuate her own waist. 'And her skin, like mine, was so soft and peachy, like a baby.'

She entered the bedroom and propped herself up against the wardrobe. We followed behind her.

'Oh, Gawd, when I saw Ginger back in Hollywood a short while back I couldn't believe the mess she'd become – eating ice-cream, and so big that the fat was spilling outta that wheelchair.' She dabbed her eyes. 'Oh, I bent over the poor thing. "Ginger," I said, "you wouldn't remember Mildred Shay, would you?" She wept with glee and looked me right in the eyes and said, "How could I have forgotten Mildred Shay?" Oh, l'amour, l'amour.'

Mildred finally turned to Joanna and they shook hands. Joanna's manner was incongruously formal and sedate in comparison.

Mildred kept looking me up and down like a search-light. 'I'm gonna love it!' she winked. She looked back at Joanna. 'Oh, honey, your little voice is so sweet – that's some kind of country twang you've got, like those country people on *Emmerdale Farm*, right? Tell me, does your family work on the land?'

There was a hint of a smile as Joanna informed Mildred she was originally from the West Country, Gloucestershire, but had lived in London 'for an age!' Emphatic, Joanna looked at me and back at Mildred, who made no attempt to further the conversation. I could tell Joanna hadn't quite made up her mind on Mildred.

Mildred placed her can of soda on the chest of drawers and wiggled over to the window and tried to open it. The window was shielded by limp powder-blue curtains which hung pathetically on a plastic track. There was a snap underfoot, and Mildred looked down at the re-mains of curtain hooks. 'Oh, Gawd, would you look at that, all broken up.'

Behind the curtains hung shredded yellowing nets, which added to the feeling of decay. I joined Mildred at the window and pushed the curtains aside with my hand. The curtain lining fell apart at my touch and made a sound rather like that of a tissue being pulled from its cardboard box. Mildred watched as the curtains disintegrated. She held the lifeless material to her bosom. 'These were from Peter Jones and cost a fortune.' I looked at the curtains, at Mildred, and then at an open-mouthed Joanna who laughed and mouthed to me, 'A long time ago?' Mildred didn't notice.

I gave the wooden window-frame a bang with the palm of my hand, once, twice, louder and harder until it opened with a creak. I forced it open, wider and wider. I pushed back both sets of curtains further. A cold breeze rushed in, and as it entered the room the fringe on the overhead light-shade danced merrily.

Mildred delighted in letting Joanna know she preferred only men and suggested all women were jealous of her beauty.

'I like men too,' Joanna retorted. In an attempt to shine, Mildred reeled off a long list of female Hollywood neighbours whom she felt had been jealous of the interest shown in her by the likes of John Gilbert, resident clown Robert Benchley, and even Rachmaninoff.

The mention of the composer had a new effect on Joanna. Her asking Mildred questions about him lifted Mildred's mood. But in seconds Mildred brought their conversation back to sex. Judging by Mildred's comments, it was doubtful she knew anything about Rachmaninoff at all, as she likened him to Richard Clayderman and Elton John.

Mildred looked pleased with herself as she stood there, slurping her soda. 'I don't think we had an affair,' she added pensively.

Joanna sniggered at the thought of Mildred enticing

Elton John. Mildred huffed. 'Gay or not, when I worked with Rudolf Nureyev on the film *Valentino* we got along famously!' She puffed out her chest. 'Let me tell you, he and I had a moment in the john.'

Joanna laughed again; Mildred didn't. Instead, she focused on me, and suggested perhaps all her raunchiness was causing me to blush. She was miffed when I told her it wasn't.

It transpired that it was at the Garden of Allah that she first had witnessed the pursuits of pleasure and the pitfalls of the picture business. As Mildred moved about the room, nosing into our bags, she talked at us of how she'd seen Gary Cooper and Joel McCrea laying naked poolside, and then diving in: 'their Johnny dingle-dangles flip-flopping about!' Mildred smirked at me as she put her lips suggestively to the can. 'Cooper was a dish, but an odd one – he liked to stuff animals.'

'I didn't know that, Mildred – taxidermy, you mean?' I asked, trying to steer her away from naked men.

'Taxi-what?' She stared blankly. 'Oh, I hear ya, oh, yes, that's it, taxidermy, oh, sure, Gary Cooper stuffed bunnies and critters, and he'd then stuff Clara Bow and some of the boys too!' She roared. 'Oh, he was naughty, and she once entertained an entire American football team in her cottage. Imagine all that throbbing muscle!' She roared even louder with laughter. 'Oh, my life! You couldn't make it up!' She looked about her. 'I have everything now but money.' She sat down on the corner of the bed and sighed deeply. The room was quiet.

Having sensed her melancholy, I asked that she tell me more of her time at the Garden of Allah. Tapping the bed, she asked me to sit. Joanna left the room for the loo on the other side of the hall, and Mildred re-launched her story.

The Garden of Allah was *the* place to live in Hollywood, located at the top of Sunset Boulevard. It had been built and owned by former silent star Alla Nazimova, who'd originally intended the sprawling estate to be her house. The stock market crash and the arrival of the 'talkies' had put pay to her dream. She had been forced to chop up her home into apartments and bunga-lows, and ended up living in what she'd intended to be her walk-in wardrobe. 'What a tragedy, being in stuck the closet,' sighed Mildred.

'That's sad, Mildred,' I said.

'I mean, honey, I've known a lot people in the closet, but that poor woman.' She shook the soda can and then looked at me. 'Well, that's Hollywood! Oh, Gawd, the people I knew, and the stories I have…Fun stuff, let's not be sad,' she said, smiling.

Mildred got to her feet, tossed the empty can into a wastepaper basket under the window and wiggled out of view.

Joanna reappeared, quiet, and started unpacking. She piled clothes onto the bed and lined up pairs of shoes on the floor. We both moved about the bedroom in silence.

It was not ten minutes before Mildred came back. Her arrival was met by a loud tut from Joanna. Mildred stood beside the bed and, like a sniffer dog, was all over our baggage. She poked fun at our mismatched luggage and told us how she'd travelled with Louis Vuitton trunks with a clothes rail and drawers inside, complete with a secret compartment for valuables. She'd had a French maid, Pekingese dogs, and a chauffeur.

'Yes, but so clunky and heavy though, no wheelie-cases back then,' Joanna quipped.

'Oh, we had wheels for the trunks, dear, but we had men to push 'em,' said Mildred.

Mildred continued to chat non-stop whilst eyeing up Joanna's clothes as Joanna pulled them out of the bags. Mildred intermittently passed comment: the green blouse deemed a difficult colour on any skin tone, the yellow summer dress not good for her pale complexion.

We were saved by the bell. Mildred was still in full throttle, so didn't hear the loud buzzing from the wall-mounted entry phone in the hall. The interruption was quite welcome. Joanna was obviously getting frustrated with Mildred's fashion critique.

It buzzed again. Joanna pointed it out. Mildred didn't hear her. The buzzer seemed to get louder.

'The phone, Mildred!' shouted Joanna.

Mildred turned on her heel and fetched it, visibly annoyed, as if the phone ringing had upstaged her just as she'd launched into a story about being propositioned by Cubby 'James Bond' Broccoli's cousin Pat De Cicco. ('He'd drugged the vodka martinis. I only drank milk so never missed a thing.') There was another buzz and another before she finally answered it.

'Hello! Hello! This is Mildred.' She repeated herself over and over before slamming the receiver down. Twiddling with her hearing aids, she looked at Joanna, and told her she must have been mistaken. The phone buzzed again.

Mildred grabbed it. 'Hello!' she shouted, accidentally pulling off her diamanté clip-on earring in her fluster. 'Oh, shit…Hello! Hello!' she screeched as she looked down at the receiver, increasingly annoyed as it continued to steal her moment: the arrival of 'youth', moreover the arrival of a man – the arrival of me.

Joanna stepped in abruptly and took the phone from Mildred's hand, which left her put out. We both heard a man's voice.

Mildred gave Joanna an icy stare. 'Well, they'll never understand you with that accent if they can't understand me,' she said, and she took back the phone and passed it instead to me. The line was dead. Mildred headed off to the living room to watch another one of her TV shows.

Less than a quarter of an hour later there was a knock on the front door. Joanna opened it to reveal a stout man wearing a uniform of grey flannels and a navy blazer with gold buttons. His complexion was ruddy. He had a comb-over and gold-framed glasses. This turned out to be Larry, the long-suffering concierge.

Larry stood firm in the doorway and appeared unwilling to cross the threshold. When Mildred re-emerged from the living room, he pointed to the intercom, his manner fierce.

'Madam, didn't you hear me on the phone?' he shouted slowly, to make sure she heard every word. His accent was thick Belfast.

'Oh, Larry, how darling of you to call – I've had a cold – flu or something – and my ears are still stuffed up,' she said politely, as her hearing aids whistled.

Despite Larry wishing her a speedy recovery, he was

in no mood for any sweet talking. The residents were his priority and he was obviously not keen on strangers taking the liberty of parking in one of his spaces.

Mildred tried to sweeten him up as she moved about the doorway as if gearing up for a pole-dance. 'Oh, Larry, honey, don't be a meanie, come in for a martini, let's have a party.' Despite her merriment Larry was unmoved. Mildred changed tactics.

'Oh, shit, Larry,' she said loudly, 'the neighbours can go screw themselves.' With her hand on hip and in her mid-Atlantic accent, she raised her voice. 'Listen Larry, my last husband, Captain Geoffrey Steele, was at Eton with two Dukes of Westminster and we've lived here since 1976, so you can't tell me what I can and can't do. We own this flat, I practically own the whole darn block!'

Larry's bark was sharp. Aware that this was getting nasty, Joanna jumped in. She apologised for our error and thanked him for putting us straight. All the while, I worried over how much it would cost to park my jalopy on a meter in Belgravia.

Mildred looked at Joanna and then at Larry. 'She's from the country.'

Larry looked blankly at Mildred and then Joanna. He softened ever so slightly. He allowed us to park for another hour, suggesting nearby Pimlico as a cheaper option than parking on Ebury Street. 'But don't be going asking me for change,' he added. 'I'm not the NatWest!'

Mildred turned to Joanna and then back to Larry, and her false lashes flashed furiously. 'Oh, shit! Well, thank-you very much, I don't think. I'm a sick woman and these kids are looking after me…Oh, wait a minute, I think I'm having a moment. Oh, I'm feeling sick,' she said, as she all but fell into my arms. With Larry one side of her and me the other, we helped Mildred into the living room. She almost pulled Larry on top of her as she fell into her recliner. Joanna fanned her with the *Radio Times*.

Mildred having settled, Joanna followed a beet-root-faced Larry to the lift. As they waited for it, I heard Joanna ask Larry where in Ireland he was from. It was just like her to use a distraction. I heard her mention Cork as they stepped into the lift car. They were laughing as the lift doors closed. I turned around to find Mildred directly behind me.

'So,' she huffed, 'that Larry has found a younger model.' I laughed it off. Mildred's mood soon lifted too as she faced me alone in the hallway. 'I'm not gonna let him make me sick,' she said. She slammed the front door and then looked at me. 'We'll have fun, you and me.' She stroked my face slowly – I felt a large diamond ring on my cheek. With that she pulled away and wiggled off to the kitchen in a way reminiscent of Marilyn Monroe on the station platform in *Some Like It Hot*. 'Shit!' she said loudly from the kitchen. 'I need a drink.' She appeared moments later at the bedroom door with two vodka martinis in crystal cocktail glasses, in spite of the fact it was not yet noon. 'Let's have a drink to celebrate your arrival,' she said. We chinked our glasses together.

Joanna returned to the flat and found us sitting on the bed.

'Oh, Joanna, darling,' said Mildred, as she polished off her drink, 'Your husband and I, we've been in the sack.' Mildred slapped my knee, got to her feet, and disappeared to the living room. The blast of the TV told me she was settling down.

As Joanna and I prepared to head out to Sainsbury's next to Victoria Station, Mildred stopped us. 'You know, Orstin,' said Mildred, as Joanna pulled on a jacket and grabbed her bag, 'country folk are the best, aren't they? My husband Geoffrey's old nanny was a country woman and he adored her.' She looked at Joanna. 'I think I'll adore you,' she said, and she gave her a hug, which put Joanna at ease. With Joanna's back to me, Mildred raised her gaze towards me, her false-eyelash wink slow and seductive. It's only temporary, I told myself. I couldn't know then what journey was in store.

Two

Clothes and Conquests

*M*ildred woke up before us each morning. She was determined that Joanna and I, but particularly I, should not see her without her 'face on.' My alarm clock read 6:00 a.m. I'd heard her bustling about during the first week of our stay and wondered what she was up to. I stood, unnoticed, in the doorway of our room, rubbing my eyes as I watched Mildred emerge from hers, her bed-head wild, her dressing gown oversized. Judging by its vintage, she'd shrunk since she got it – the diminutive figure before me looked like Yoda in a blonde wig.

She bypassed the bathroom sink and headed directly to her make-up kit. The routine was simply to plaster on more pan-stick, cake on more mascara, and add lashings of lipstick using a Bakelite lipstick brush fashioned for her by Max Factor himself. He, along with hairdresser Sydney Guilaroff, beautified Mildred, Joan Crawford, Norma Shearer, Judy Garland, Paulette Goddard, Myrna Loy and countless others every day in the famed pink and white cosmetic rooms within Metro-Goldwyn-Mayer. The MGM motto coined by the studio's publicity department, 'More Stars Than There Are In The Heavens', was etched on a placard on the wall above the dressing table. Mildred was the only one left alive now from that gilded sorority.

Her nightwear was varied at best. To bed, she wore oversized T-shirts picked up by Baby at Walmart in Los Angeles. One featured the *Care Bears*; another, baskets of forget-me-nots.

In the daytime, around the house, Mildred mostly wore nightgowns, frothy David Nieper numbers in soft pastel blue, buttercup yellow, and Barbara Cartland pink, edged with lace, ribbons and bows. Mildred's favourite was a lilac nighty trimmed with mink, over which she wore either flowing Chinese silk or rich satin dressing gowns with scalloped cuffs, the get-up finished off with marabou-feathered slippers. The overall effect was pure Jean Harlow, but by 2002 the glamorous garments were tired, torn, stapled to fit her shrinking frame – and overall, a bit grubby.

What was often most amusing to Joanna and me was Mildred's choice of daywear. She admitted that it was only on our moving in that she even bothered to get dressed in day-clothes at all. Joanna and I would take jokey bets on what would greet us sitting in the recliner when we got back to the flat. Her Greek outfit was particularly memorable: its traditional piped embroidered skirt with matching waist-coat top half, under which she wore an off-the-shoulder billowing white blouse. Then there was the Pucci dress and her Susan Small floral ensembles. The lilac pantsuit was special too. However, she stopped wearing it after watching a fashion item on the magazine show *This Morning* about 'women with problem camel-toe'. To her horror, she realised whilst reapplying her make-up in the long bathroom mirror, later that same afternoon, that she too was a casualty, and spent the remainder of the day trying to get an emergency appointment with her doctor.

With no money to spend on clothes, she considered these and other ensembles faultless – aside from the pant suit. However, to an outsider, Mildred, the once-glamourous movie star who'd been dressed by famed Hollywood costumiers Adrian Greenberg, Edith Head, and Irene Lentz, looked like a poster girl for a rather drab charity shop. Mildred's much-mentioned complaint of having 'everything but money' couldn't have been more apparent.

* * *

When Joanna and I surfaced on weekday mornings, Mildred welcomed us both with a cheery 'good morning,' sitting in her recliner sipping Lady Grey tea, her Bible (including a prayer list of her friends whom she deemed to need it) resting on the right arm of the recliner. Rosebud was curled up on her lap and Dermot Murnaghan was on the television.

As Joanna sat at the dining table to wolf down Rice Krispies and a mug of tea, while I had a banana and Marmite on toast, Mildred came over to recount dreams – usually erotic ones – from the previous night: tales of her lying in her 'gorgeous hunk of a husband Geoffrey's arms' or, on other occasions, a shopping list of Hollywood beefcakes. There were instances when she'd mention her long-ago first husband, Irishman

Thomas Frances Murphy ('He was a better-looking Gene Kelly'), or her second husband, the handsome playboy Winthrop 'Winny' Gardner Junior, the fourteenth proprietor of Gardiners Island, New York. She'd shout at us from the recliner, over Carol Kirkwood's *BBC Breakfast* weather forecast at full volume, with tales of her libidinous self in times gone by.

Mildred liked to talk about sex, or 'fucking' as she called it – unless speaking about Geoffrey. They didn't fuck, they made love. Mildred also liked to shock, although quite often she was less shocking and instead rather naïve.

'My darling, handsome husband Geoffrey was rock solid every morning, just for me,' she told Joanna shortly after our arrival, on an outing to the Photo-Me machine at Victoria Railway Station. She wanted to have a passport-sized photo taken in order to renew her bus pass – the irony being that Mildred never took the bus: buses were for old people and full of germs. Mildred wasn't keen on either of the aforementioned. 'Imagine it,' she had called to Joanna from behind the curtain, loud enough for inquisitive stares. 'Every morning, every single morning he was up just for me.' Joanna played along.

'That's amazing, Mildred – what magnetism you had,' Joanna said, giggling.

* * *

It was a rare occasion that Mildred and Joanna 'bonded'. Mildred was trying her best to crack 'girl time'. They sat in Starbucks, laughing over the disastrous photos

(Mildred had had the stool in the booth too low, and as a result anything below her pencilled-in eyebrows wasn't visible). Then Mildred suddenly observed the lace-up brogues Joanna was wearing.

'Tell me, dear, does Orstin like those shoes?' she asked, and looked slightly horrified at Joanna.

'These, oh, they're so comfy. I do a lot of walking in school,' smiled Joanna.

'Oh, really? You like wearing boys' shoes? I couldn't wear anything that didn't have a heel,' she said.

The pair abandoned the idea of photos for the bus pass. Mildred was only ever shot by the Hollywood masters, preferring Clarence Sinclair Bull or Horst P. Horst, and felt the photobooth just didn't work for her. 'The lighting is all wrong, darling,' she told Joanna as they walked past the Army & Navy store on Victoria Street. 'Maybe I should see if Horst is still working, or perhaps try David Bailey?' I'd noticed Horst's name and address written in the address book she kept by her pocket-book. It was scrawled underneath that of Alfred Hitchcock on St. Cloud Drive, Bel-Air, and Katharine Hepburn on the Upper East Side.

Mildred slowed down as she and Joanna strolled past a window display of shoes. Mildred decided a pair of four-inch Perspex peep-toes would suit Joanna's dainty feet, and what was more, appeal much more to her man – to me. Joanna did her best to convince Mildred that her choice of footwear was impractical. But Mildred was never practical, so they argued.

There would be worse blows to come. For one thing, Mildred couldn't stand feminists. 'Shit, if I met that

Germaine Greer female I'd kick her right in the fanny!'
Joanna was a feminist, but on that occasion didn't take
the bait.

* * *

So we wouldn't disturb her lengthy afternoons in front
of the TV – her selection of favourite shows circled in
red pen in her *Daily Express* newspaper guide – Mildred
lent us a door key each. It made sense and saved us from
being stranded on the doorstep, trying to make her hear
us over the intercom. Joanna had been marooned on
the doorstep twice, unable to get Mildred to hear her
ringing the buzzer or the landline. Larry the porter reluctantly let her into the building. Larry didn't like 'the
boy', as Mildred fondly referred to me. I felt him eye me
with suspicion – perhaps he agreed with Lady Myrtle,
a grand lady on the second floor who had warned Mildred, on discovering Joanna and I had moved in, that
we might be gold diggers.

Mildred had laughed as she recounted Lady Myrtle's
worries. 'Gold diggers! Darlings, the gold has been
spent, I've hardly a nickel.'

On the first occasion that Joanna was stranded at
the main entrance, Larry escorted her right up to Mildred's front door, opening it with his spare key, and
then marched Joanna right into the living room where
Mildred was sitting watching *Family Affairs*, the volume
so high that everything in the room rattled. Mildred's
concentration was so fixed that she didn't hear either
of them, even when they shouted from the doorway.

Joanna told me when I got home how Mildred squealed when she did finally notice them, laughing off her momentary deafness with the excuse of a slight cold. Mildred was desperate not to appear incapacitated and was livid that Joanna had involved Larry. It took a good hour for Joanna (or 'the female' as Mildred labelled her if and when they fell out) to be forgiven. Mildred had no choice: the aroma from the kitchen of freshly made hamburgers and potato wedges sizzling away had Mildred drooling in all of ten seconds.

Prior to our arrival, with Larry off her dance card, she had briefly considered Abdul, the rake-thin twenty-something nephew of Mr Ali: easy prey.

Mildred liked the exotic, or so she'd told me as she watched George Alagiah co-present the *BBC Six O'Clock News* alongside Sophie Raworth, of whom she was less fond – not so much Sophie Raworth herself, but her hair. Nobody wore their hair quite like Mildred. Mildred thought Sophie would benefit from her style advice. Joanna and I tired of the repeat pattern: every time Sophie came onscreen, Mildred would announce that she intended to pen the girl a letter, suggesting she wear more lipstick and enclosing a photo of her own magnificent coiffure.

George Alagiah, she told me, reminded her of Mehmet Hayri Rüştü, one of the first industrialists of the Republic of Turkey, the famous 'King of Sugar', otherwise dubbed 'Atatürk's Contractor'. Apparently, he had fallen madly in love with Mildred when in Hollywood visiting his playboy son, Ali Ipar.

Mildred had retained the Sugar King's love letters as

proof of their affair. One evening, as Joanna and I were clearing away the dinner things, Mildred retrieved his letters from a drawer in the bottom of one of the Louis Vuitton trunks. She proceeded to read dozens at full volume over *Eastenders*, seated in her recliner as we were washing up in the kitchen. Joanna surprised her later that night when she found, amongst the clutter in an old Harrods hat-box, a cassette tape of Nancy Sinatra's catchy hit *Sugar Town*. Mildred laughed and laughed, as did we, and the three of us sang and danced about the living room – Rosebud hiding under the dining table. Mildred, of course, claimed to have the better voice as she belted out:

I got some troubles, but they won't last.
I'm gonna lay right down here in the grass
And pretty soon all my troubles will pass,
'Cause I'm in shoo-shoo-shoo-, shoo-shoo, shoo
Shoo-shoo-shoo-shoo, shoo-shoo Sugar Town.

Other times when Mildred watched the news, she likened George Alagiah to Porfirio 'Rubi' Rubirosa, one of the greatest playboys, she told me, of the twentieth century. She'd watched him play polo – after one game she told me he'd asked if she could 'follow him around the back' in order to remove his boots. 'The darnedest thing was, Orstin,' she said in hysterics, 'the boots were the only things that stayed on!'

* * *

All those in Mildred's immediate vicinity were led to believe that Mildred was in good shape when they telephoned her. Despite being a dreadful hypochondriac, Mildred knew how to put on an act. For the sake of Baby, if not herself, she maintained the attitude that 'the show must go on.' But when we arrived, Mildred finally started to go out. Joanna would take her for a wander around the block, or the two of us would take her for a cuppa. When neighbour Lady Pamela Davidson saw Mildred, only days prior to our arrival, being picked up by hospital transport for an eye appointment, she was shocked at her thin frame, disguised as it always was under a mink coat. She was convinced we had probably saved Mildred from death by malnutrition. Lady Davidson stopped me in the carpark one day when we had been living with Mildred for a while, having seen Joanna taking Mildred out earlier in the day. She and Lord Davidson had never seen 'the old girl' looking so good. Both were certain that Mildred had been masking for years what was really going on – loneliness.

As time marched on and Mildred became more buoyant, one never knew what to expect when coming home and stepping over the threshold after a day's work. She'd excitedly welcome me into the living room with a martini, sharing a memory that had come flooding back and which she'd scribbled down on a jotter-pad kept close at hand, or tell me about a phone call she'd made to an old co-star. Everyone she spoke to was judged older than she, less lucid, less fun, be it her former MGM co-star Suzanne Kaaren or her old sparring partners Selene Walters and Zsa Zsa Gabor.

* * *

Mildred disappeared into the small spare bedroom closet next to the living room. She materialised minutes later with freshly-applied lipstick in a cloud of Giorgio Beverly Hills perfume. Humming to herself, she proceeded to flop into the recliner and flip up the footrest. I watched her as I cleared our dinner plates and her tray away. Footrest down again, Mildred hunted around in a giant Lloyds Pharmacy bag.

'Now, wait a minute. Where the hell are you?' she said, her head almost lost inside the carrier bag.

Still watching her as I scurried to and from the kitchen, I saw Mildred had found a box of Rennies. She pressed one and then a second tablet from its silver foil casing, munching on them as if they were sweets. Despite protesting at the size of the portion of chicken korma, rice, and naan bread that Joanna had presented her with earlier, she'd polished off the lot.

As with every meal time since we had arrived twelve days before, Mildred had refused to join us at the dining table. She preferred to remain in her recliner and eat breakfast (muesli and yoghurt), lunch (usually a Cup-a-Soup), and her evening meal hunched over a tray upon a collapsible table in front of her old Grundig television set. Her firm TV favourites were *BBC Breakfast* and soap operas: *Doctors, Family Affairs, Emmerdale, Coronation Street* and *Eastenders*. The pattern was repeated over and over. Mildred always left a clean plate and complimented Joanna on every culinary delight, be it steak and kidney pie or her mum's fish pie recipe. Despite my advice that her choice of dining area wasn't good for her digestion, Mildred wouldn't be moved. Rennies were the Mildred Shay equivalent of an After Eight mint.

After dinner most evenings, I cleared away the place-mats and water glasses while Joanna was in the kitchen washing up; then Mildred insisted I sit with her, the television on full volume. She'd taken a liking to a line said by Barbara Windsor as Peggy Mitchell, the pub landlady and family matriarch in *Eastenders*: 'But we're family,' she said jubilantly, before she rubbed her chest and burped, and reached for another Rennie.

With a tea-towel flung over my shoulder, I perched opposite her in a pink library chair, the arms cut to ribbons. The culprit appeared: Rosebud. She set about positioning herself at the foot of the recliner, her claws outstretched as she licked each one in slow motion. I felt as if she were warning me she possessed a weapon, observing me with a look of pure hatred.

Mildred caught me watching her prized pussy. 'Oh, now, Orstin, darling,' she shouted over *Eastenders*, 'Rosebud is Mamma's pride and joy, Mamma's little baby-girl, and she don't much like having competition!'

Seemingly Rosebud knew Mildred was talking about her. 'Oh, come on, Orstin, we're family,' she said again. Rosebud jumped onto Mildred's lap, turned one way and then the other, and settled. She was soon dozing. It wasn't long before Mildred dozed off too. Her story of auditioning for a role on the then-new soap *Emmerdale Farm*, back in the 70s, could wait to be completed. It later turned out Mildred had turned down the part be-cause her daughter Baby had wanted her in California.

Mildred would regret not having become more of a household name.

I joined Joanna in the kitchen. We decided that, once everything was cleared away and she had completed some reading in preparation for her school placement in East Ham the next day, we would go for a drink at the local pub, The Duke of Wellington on Elizabeth Street. Mildred had told me that the small but usually busy establishment had been favoured by 'my darling, dearest, and most cherished husband Geoffrey.' Nicknamed The Duke of Boots by Geoffrey, the pub had been a favourite haunt of his long after they had first moved into the Cundy Street flats in 1976. Later, a chatty pub regular told me Geoffrey had gone to the pub nightly, spending Mildred's shrinking fortune flirting with barmaids, Lady Lucan, actor Richard Greene, Winston Churchill's daughter Sarah, and a member of the Du-Pont family who, like Geoffrey, had squandered family wealth on whiskey.

As the weekend approached, Joanna announced we would help Mildred by tidying the living room. Unable to move for clutter, and with Joanna barely able to breathe due to the sheer amount of cat hair and dust, we dedicated our entire third Saturday in the flat to clearing and cleaning. However, by the end of the day, it was Mildred who had wiped the floor with Joanna.

Three

The Great Clean

$\mathcal{J}$oanna and I had already christened the small and jumbled spare bedroom Mildred's 'make-up room'. When we had first arrived, Mildred had chosen to keep this space on her tour of the flat until last. We had stood wide-eyed and open-mouthed in her shadow. The door was prevented from opening fully by a bank of old Louis Vuitton trunks, golf clubs and a tartan golf bag, a rowing machine, and a standard lamp with buckled shade and tatty fringe.

'Now, dears, I've got a feeling there's a darling little bed in here,' she said in all seriousness as she surveyed the hoard, seemingly unperturbed by the musty-smelling tableau before us. We did eventually find a wooden bed frame and mattress pushed into the corner under a partially covered window, limp purple curtains puckered by the mountain of jumble. There were bundles of clothes, some stuffed in carrier bags from long-ago London shops: Bourne & Hollingsworth and Simpsons of Piccadilly; more jammed-in bags from defunct LA department stores, I. Maglins and Bullocks. A holdall split at the seams spilt out its contents: men's suit jackets and flannels. Half-a-dozen shoe holders that hung from the doors of over-stuffed closets contained an Imelda

33

Marcos-style stockpile of stilettos, cork wedges and Ferragamo flats.

On the left of the make-up room, against the wall, stood a giant dark wood dressing table with a mirror surround, like those in old movies with light bulbs around it. Eight of the fifteen bulbs had blown. Two were missing altogether. The lacquered surface was flecked with remnants of lipstick and face powder, a tacky mess on which were propped up photographs of her husband Geoffrey, daughter Baby, and of Mildred in her Hollywood years with Cary Grant and Alan Ladd. The backs of the frames were missing or held together by Sellotape.

At first glance, Joanna thought the carpet underfoot was home to a colony of spiders; however, she was comforted when I pointed out the creepy-crawlies were actually old fallen false eyelashes.

The make-up room took a full weekend – literally from dawn till dusk – to sort, tidy, and clean. Mildred made the odd guest appearance, removing tat from the black bin bags into which we were putting it: buttons from an old blouse perhaps useful as toys for Rosebud, a zip from a pair of Geoffrey's old slacks reusable for sure, the fronts of tea-dresses ideal for dusters, and a dozen pairs of mouldy three-inch heels deemed suitable to send to 'poor black kiddies in Africa'. When I argued that they'd hardly be suitable footwear for a rugged landscape, Mildred agreed and stuffed them back in their cloth pouches.

Joanna decided to decamp Mildred to her bedroom. Having her out of the way would make the clean-up easier. I also rather cunningly proposed that she'd love the surprise – a final big reveal. Mildred played along.

'Oh, darling, what a marvellous idea, and how clever of you to be able to clean. I've never *done* domestic,' she said, in all seriousness. 'Mother had a Russian ex-countess clean for her at the house in Cedarhurst.'

I had located an ancient upright vacuum cleaner right at the back of the huge cupboard in the hall and set to work. Mildred came back, intrigued by the noise, stood open-mouthed as if a revelation were unfolding. Soon she demanded to take her turn on the vacuum cleaner, giggling as she did so. 'Look, look, in and out and in and out...Oh, I feel like I'm doing a Jane Fonda workout!' she said excitedly.

The laughter ended when Mildred became alarmed at watching Joanna take puffs from her blue inhaler. The dust, laughter, and Rosebud were the reasons for her wheezing. Mildred was convinced otherwise, certain that Joanna's allergies must come from her being a 'country girl' and not used to London air, although we both told her Joanna had been in London since her university days. She'd also decided that Joanna's skills at 'making home' meant she was perfect housewife material for me.

But after her initial excitement about the vacuum, she quietly asked that we sit down. Mildred had something she needed to say. It turned out Mildred did in fact already have a 'maid', as she called her, and her name was Resheda. (Mildred had re-christened her 'Re-shit-a'.)

'You've gotta be kidding me,' laughed Joanna, and looked about the decay.

Mildred was not kidding. As it turned out, Re-shit-a didn't so much as lift a duster, and because there was no washing machine in the flat, when Resheda did arrive, Mildred sent her directly to the launderette off the Pimlico Road to wash Mildred's essentials. On her return, Resheda would be tasked with making coffee with a splash of Tia Maria, and then she would sit as Mildred gave Resheda advice on her sex life.

'I tell you,' Mildred told us, 'I'm better than that female, Dr Ruth, on the television.'

Mildred revealed that it was following a particularly bad turn of labyrinthitis that an interfering 'female' locum at the doctor's surgery had got her assessed by Social Services. The upside was that she received housing benefit, to cover her peppercorn rent paid to the Duke of Westminster. The downside: she was given a home help. That was when Resheda had appeared on the scene.

Mildred hadn't had to worry about Resheda until now, as she'd been away in Tehran visiting relatives. Mildred told Joanna and I that she'd decided to lie to Social Services, telling them she'd be in the country for a month with her friend Norah, Lady Docker, to make sure they didn't send a Resheda replacement.

Joanna got up from the library chair, clearly – and quite rightly – scared that Social Services might find out that we were staying with her. She was frightened they could perhaps put a stop to the benefits that were covering Mildred's rent. Even though we weren't actually giving Mildred any money for lodging with her, we were paying the bills and buying all the food for us and Rosebud.

This bombshell added further complications to my now-strained relationship with Joanna. We argued: Joanna was cross that my on-off income had put us – no, her – in such an awkward and precarious predicament. Mildred broke up the fight. She reassured Joanna that Social Services would never sniff Norah out because Norah had been dead twenty years. What was more, if Social Services did arrive, she'd play ignorant. Mildred patted Joanna on the arm; she'd perhaps forgotten Mildred was a good actress. 'My dear, one must not forget Barry Norman wrote that my performance as Janet Roscoe in *Inspector Morse* was more boorish than John Thaw himself.'

So it was that that weekend Mildred cooked up a plan: if anyone should ask, we were Mildred's relatives from the country, more specifically Hampton Court. Mildred had a knack of easing tension without knowing it. Joanna and I laughed at the suggestion that Hampton Court was the countryside. But Mildred had made up her mind. Geoffrey's old nanny had lived at the Palace during the War, and it had taken an age to get there, and besides, Mildred had seen a pig on the manicured lawn, a goat, and a queer fella in gum-boots. 'I'm telling you, it was like another world,' she said.

In time we would meet Resheda. On the first occasion, Mildred had forgotten she was coming. When she heard her voice on the intercom, Mildred panicked. She locked our bedroom door so Resheda couldn't tell she had long-term 'visitors', and suggested perhaps I hide in the toilet whilst Mildred entertain her in the living room. When I refused, she suggested she should tie me up on the bed.

'Mildred! It's a cleaner from Social Services, not a Russian spy.' Either way, Mildred wasn't happy having Resheda sniffing around.

* * *

With cleaning materials purchased, and buckets of soapy water and black sacks at the ready, Joanna and I inched Mildred from her recliner. We then removed the surrounding medley of medicine packets, newspapers, make-up, scrapbooks, and finally, under sufferance, Rosebud.

Crowded and chaotic, the living room was dominated by a wide expanse of windows running the length of the room. The daylight was masked by yellowing net curtains. Directly opposite and mirroring the windows was a smooth angular concrete fireplace, and above that were three gargantuan Chinese wall-hangings, sun-bleached, most likely from long ago. Mildred told me these had been amongst her father's most prized possessions. Like everything else in the flat they had a glimmer of past glory. But time had marched on, and with little or no up-keep, the hangings were left to rot on rusted nails.

'Aren't they gorgeous?' Mildred said, animated, re-appearing in the door-way after only ten minutes in exile. She tip-toed around a bookcase I'd moved, the pink library chair, and her exercise bike. 'They hung in Daddy's Palm Beach mansion,' she said, scrutinising their faded splendour. 'Daddy was the cleverest man in America. His brain was bigger than anyone's,' she said emphatically. 'Daddy was much smarter, much brighter, I thought, than that filthy-looking friend of his,' she added.

While I sensed I knew exactly who Mildred was talking about, I asked the question anyway.

'Yes, darling,' she said, hand on hip. 'That's the man – Einstein.'

'And yet Daddy didn't teach you to use a hoover,' said Joanna sarcastically, as she waved away clouds of dust stirred up by my moving furniture. Mildred looked over to Joanna, but was too focused on the hangings to have registered the comment.

'I'd put money, if I had it, on these coming from some big noise like the Mings!' Her jubilation suddenly faded as she faced the crumbling hangings. 'Oh, dear,' she sighed, repeating herself. 'I've everything but money, everything but money.'

Mildred manoeuvred around the library chair and sat. She described her former childhood home with its thirty rooms: 'Everything glistened,' she said, her eyes wide as she reminisced.

Like a child marvelling over drawings in an adventure book, Mildred spoke of her rich and powerful Daddy, who'd purchased the hangings whilst he and Lillian took a tour of Shanghai. They had filled three suites at the Astor House Hotel and then, when they set sail, two large cabins aboard the HMS *Queen Mary*. They collected treasures at antique markets, or trophies, like the giant white tiger, golden-haired monkey, and deer he'd shot on hunting trips. A local furrier had turned the white tiger into a rug for the library at the

Shays' Cedarhurst estate, New York. As Mildred talked, it was clear she was proud of her father's affluence.

Her zeal for a life that was now past was only made more startling as I looked about me, wondering where that life went.

'Imagine it. I have everything now but money,' she repeated.

'Well, you're in a great location here in Belgravia, Mildred,' Joanna reminded her.

Mildred looked about the room. 'Oh, yes, the address is right.' On her feet, she opted to leave us to it. I watched her saunter along the hall and back into the bedroom.

As I suspected, she couldn't keep away. 'My beautiful, perfectly heavenly Daddy was super-smart – the cleverest, richest man in America,' she said, back in the room and reaching for his photograph in a pile Joanna had moved from atop the drinks cabinet. Cross that we were not paying enough attention, Mildred raised her voice. 'Darlings, I kid you not; there was nobody brighter than Daddy.'

'Mildred, you're in the way,' said Joanna firmly, as she stepped over towards Mildred, who was suddenly tangled up in the aerial cable and TV flex. 'I'm scared you'll fall, Mildred. How about you make us some tea?'

'Tea is for nice old ladies and I ain't no nice old lady,' she giggled. Instead she suggested she make us a vodka martini. I looked at my watch: eleven. But I decided that her playing barman would give us some time.

I piled newspapers into a cardboard box for recycling and attempted to scrape mould from the windowpane using bleach, a J-Cloth and a tea-knife. Joanna fashioned a makeshift mask from a cotton scarf to tackle the velvet curtains, her hands protected by marigolds.

'The bar's open!' shouted Mildred from the kitchen. Her motive for getting us into the kitchen became clear as, with drink in hand, Mildred left us and re-entered the living room.

'Oh, what are you intending to do with the newspapers, dear?' shouted Mildred. 'I'm saving them, I feel sure I'll find coupons.'

Joanna shouted her reply: 'They're all long out of date, Mildred.' Joanna's frustration that Mildred wanted to be involved was given away by the uncharacteristic way Joanna downed her cocktail. I downed mine too. It tasted strong enough to kill a horse. I followed Joanna to the living room. Mildred was looking through photographs. She leant against the fireplace. She'd found more of her father.

'Oh, he was smart – more so than his good friends, Presidents Roosevelt and Herbert Hoover, I always thought! Daddy was a Supreme Court attorney who demanded a million dollars per case – imagine! Let me tell you something, honey, we had it – the Shay family was something else! I tell you, Daddy's chauffeur was this exiled Russian prince. Why, every time I got outta the car I felt I wanted to curtsey.' She stood upright to demonstrate. 'Hey, Orstin, reach behind you...Look there, the house in that silver frame, that's our house.' I located the photo. The house was opulent, with large columns surrounding the front door, and palm trees dotted about the drive. Mildred took the frame from me. The photo was sepia-toned, the silver badly tarnished.

'Mother had a French maid; I had a French maid; my sister Adeline had a French maid...the maids had maids! Oh, and get this, my neighbour was none other than the 'Poor Little Rich Girl' Barbara Hutton; we were real pals. Isn't that funny, I've hardly given her a thought for years until now. Oh, I tell you, Orstin, you are getting me to tell stories...oh, you are wheedling them outta me.'

Joanna decided the only way we would make headway was if I accompanied Mildred to her bedroom whilst she cleaned alone. Mildred agreed to this, but first stopped off in the kitchen to fix us both with refills. She talked of President Hoover stopping by for dinner, and 'that sweet Woodrow Wilson', who had brought Mildred a new dolly on every visit. 'I do remember he was mean to Precious, our black maid, though,' Mildred said. 'I didn't like that about him.'

I had already witnessed the way Mildred went very over the top whenever she met a black person. In Boots at Victoria Station, she had gushed to the point of embarrassment because a black shop assistant had helped her with a prescription. On our way back to the flat, she confided in me that she'd lived with racists. 'I've a lot of sucking up to do.'

Barbara Hutton had been a friendly playmate. Mildred talked about their adventures as she swirled an ice-cube around her empty glass, threw it into the sink, poured vodka into a measure, added a smaller measure of Vermouth – her tiny hand quivered at the weight of the bottle – then repeated the process again, before she tossed the empty measure back towards the sink and dropped in four olives: two each. The loud clatter startled Rosebud, who had come in from the bedroom to use the cat litter tray.

'Bottoms up!' toasted Mildred, not getting the irony as she knocked her drink back. I followed suit. The smell of Rosebud defecating and the strength of the drink made me feel woozy. Taking her arm, I guided Mildred towards the bedroom, but she had other ideas, and forcefully took me in the opposite direction.

'Joanna, dear, what are you doing now?' Her tone changed when she entered the room. 'Oh, my dear, what's that?'

I followed her gaze towards the windows where, before our exit to the kitchen, there had been net curtains, albeit the bottoms just thin shreds – thanks to Rosebud. The curtains were now heaped on the floor. After a few cross words as to what should become of these, Mildred decided they should be donated to charity, so that – in her words – some 'poor unfortunate African kiddies' could make head-pieces and shawls to wear to church.

With Joanna losing patience, Mildred found herself in a state as she tried to navigate around furniture, stacks of books, two giant monogrammed trunks, and an array of occasional tables. I took action and, after grabbing the bottle of vodka from the kitchen, tried to escort Mildred back into her bedroom with the suggestion that we could go through her scrapbooks. However, before I could achieve this, Mildred had an idea and headed back to Joanna, via the make-up room.

'Mildred!' said Joanna, muffled from behind her mask. 'I'm trying to help here and I can't get the job done with you in the room.'

'You're doing a wonderful thing, darling,' said Mildred, without paying Joanna much attention. 'It's just I have to make sure nothing is thrown away by mistake. Some of my things are worth millions!'

'Mildred,' I said, as I stood behind her, 'Joanna isn't going to throw anything away valuable.'

'But the newspapers, darling. I have to check for coupons, and what's in that bag there, dear?' she said, pointing to a C&A carrier bag.

'Hard dried-up cat shit,' said Joanna, clearly miffed.

'What?!' cried Mildred.

'Dried cat shit,' said Joanna, her tone sharp.

'Oh, now, how do you suppose that happened?' said Mildred, as we joined her in staring at Rosebud, who had appeared from underneath the sideboard. 'My neighbour, the Marchioness of Milford-Haven, is a cat-lover. She's so clever when it comes to anything one wants to know about cats. I should ring her.'

'Don't bother her. It's obvious, Mildred,' said Joanna. 'Rosebud has been going to the toilet behind these old trunks.' Joanna pointed to the floor. 'And it's not just a recent visit either. Why don't you let the cleaner you have *clean*?'

'Cats are clean creatures,' said Mildred primly. 'You see, if her kitty-cat box has any nasties inside it, she'll refuse to do a pee-pee or a poo-poo.' Mildred looked toward Rosebud, who was still by the sideboard. 'She's Mama's little baby-girl!'

'Maybe she needs a nappy,' I joked, trying to ease the tension.

'Nappy?' asked Mildred quizzically.

'Yes. Oh, diaper, you say diaper,' I said.

'Oh, now, my dear, I've never needed such a thing, not even for my beautiful daughter Baby. Nanny said she sat on the toilet from birth! God, she's bright. JFK said she could have been a rocket scientist!' said Mildred.

I wasn't sure which was the more fantastical: a fully toilet-trained newborn or President John F. Kennedy discussing Baby's bowel movements – even Mildred knowing JFK at all. It was growing increasingly apparent, however, that Mildred Shay had been somebody.

'Oh, so she just takes a dump over there?' said Joanna.

'We'll just have to make sure the litter tray has fresh grit then, Mildred,' I said.

As it turned out, Mildred had only been removing the clumped, soiled grit and topping up, rather than completely refreshing Rosebud's litter tray – the reason being that cat litter cost too much. Without a clean tray, Rosebud had gone elsewhere. The hard, dried-up faeces Joanna found behind the trunks, the TV, and bookcase indicated Rosebud had been toileting around the flat for some time. From then on, we bought everything Rosebud needed in that department. Despite this, Rosebud continued to take it upon herself to shit about the flat. There were deposits outside our bedroom door and the entrance to the bathroom. The worst occasion was when, on entering the flat after a day at Westminster Library researching for my obituaries, I was faced with a gut-wrenching smell. Unbeknown to her, Mildred, when wearing open-toe sling-backs, had stepped in a pile outside the make-up room and trodden it all about the flat, and then smeared it all over the footrest of the recliner.

We thought if we couldn't stop Rosebud, we could at least make the flat more habitable.

Mildred was on her feet whilst I sat on the bed. She poked around in a tall chest of drawers. 'Now, wait a minute,' she said, 'I know she's in here.' Mildred eventually found photographs of her as a child with Barbara Hutton. 'Oh, Gawd, I tell you, that little Barbara Hutton was real dirty.' She lowered her voice and, still on her feet, leant over me. 'She'd get a kick from showing her twat to boys on the beach!' She laughed loudly as she moved across to sit next to me. 'Imagine! Disgusting!' She was still laughing. 'I didn't even notice my own, but she knew hers alright! She was sexed-up at seven.' She leant in closer. 'Oh, all this raunchy talk – I'm awful!' Mildred looked at the photo of her old friend. 'Ah, we both lost fortunes…I suppose it's only money.'

Mildred proceeded to show me more photographs of the Palm Beach house, and of her in a fur coat alongside her sister Adeline, and then another shot of an interior of the house. 'Our house was as big as Barbara's – hmm, maybe even bigger,' she said, pondering over the photograph. 'Barbara hated poor people; I mean, I wasn't like that. I didn't like money. I'd say to my Daddy, "Daddy, I don't want money, it makes my pocketbook all dirty."' She roared with laughter. 'What a stupid kid! I mean, saying no to all that dough.'

Mildred and Barbara Hutton kept in contact but

were never friends. She said they'd gone to the same parties and that they were presented at Court to King George V and Queen Mary at Buckingham Palace in the same year.

She delved into the pile of photos and found one of her and her Daddy at Ascot. 'My hats were so splendid, I always had a dozen or so every season, by Lilly Daché. I'd always make the front pages – I guess the hats helped.'

With Joanna in the living room, I sat in the bedroom with Mildred and her stories. Like a Rolodex, names of monumental figures known to the family, and later to Mildred, in and out of Hollywood, rolled off her tongue.

I would come to learn that there had been a darker side to the Shays. The trigger was the traumatic death of her young brother Arnold when he was just eight. Mildred had adored Arnold, who had called her 'Cissie'. He was knocked down and killed on the road outside the Shay house by the drunken chauffeur of a ritzy neighbour. Arnold had pleaded with his mother that he be allowed to run down the driveway to greet the 'Ice Man', delivering ice to the Shays' residence and their Palm Beach neighbours. Arnold stepped out from behind the van and was killed instantly. The chauffeur was so grief-stricken that he later killed himself by driving his employer's shiny black Packard over a cliff in Malibu. Mildred was ultimately blamed by Lillian for Arnold's death. Her mother said she'd been showing off, leaving Arnold to his own devices. The afternoon following his death, Mildred decided in her young mind to bring laughter to a house filled with sadness. She'd develop and perform skits, or sing to entertain her infant sister Adeline. As Daddy's favourite, Mildred could do no wrong. In Lillian Shay's eyes, her behaviour was inappropriate and unforgivable.

The last twenty photos were all of Baby. I peeked at my watch and wondered how much longer Joanna would need.

'I'm ready,' Joanna called eventually, and then added quietly, 'Well, sort of.'

'Finally,' I said to myself.

Like she'd heard a call to arms, Mildred leapt off the bed and raced from the bedroom to the living room with me in tow.

'Oh, darling!' squealed Mildred, standing in the doorway to the living room, and repeated her praise over and over again as she looked about the rejuvenated room. I sensed her check to see if I was still behind her – and then I was confronted by Mildred seemingly fainting into my arms. After the initial shock, I wanted to applaud her performance, rather brilliantly orchestrated and surely worthy of an Academy Award for Best Performance in a 'Checking if she'll be caught before swooning' role.

'Oh, you beautiful clever country girl!' Mildred shrieked as she came round from her routine. With the back of her hand strategically placed at her temple, she clip-clopped towards Joanna in her heeled slippers and embraced her. When Joanna was finally released, Mildred left behind lipstick kisses.

'Mildred, I've lived in London for years,' said Joanna, miffed that Mildred refused to see how sophisticated she had become. Mildred didn't register it; she was in ecstasy.

In spite of the fact Joanna had only managed to clean and tidy one end of the living room, Mildred continued to weep tears of joy. Despite the interruptions, Joanna had managed to sponge down the recliner, wash ornaments, and tidy and polish the shelves. The mahogany drinks cabinet now had a shine to it and the carpet – what hadn't been devoured by moths – looked decidedly fresh from a good vacuum. Finally, the bag of Rosebud's dried up shit had been taken outside and disposed of in a redundant carrier bag. The space now gave a sign, a slight flicker, of what it might have once been. However, the jubilation was to be short-lived.

We left Mildred in the flat on the phone when Joanna and I headed out for the Duke of Boots, where we had planned to meet a friend of mine, Kirsty. Mildred was in mid-flow on the telephone to Baby in California. As I closed the door, I could hear her waxing lyrical about Joanna's housekeeping skills.

Later, Joanna and I walked Kirsty to the bus stop on Victoria Street. Joanna was happily merry; the effects of sharing a bottle of wine with Kirsty. We waved her off and walked back to the flat hand-in-hand. With Joanna the calmest I had seen her in ages, I suggested that perhaps Mildred could ask Resheda to vacuum and keep things tidy. Furthermore, as the flat was transformed, we could even ask friends over. I knew Adam and Lee and Joanna's brother Jonny and his boyfriend Justin would love Mildred. And then there was my twin brother, Howard. She would love him, and he her. There would be a very special friendship.

Joanna squeezed my hand; she was happy. Mildred's

bedroom light was on when we got home. Behind closed doors, Mildred's jubilation had changed to misgiving.

We didn't see much of Mildred the next morning. She stayed in bed longer than usual. Her mood, particularly towards Joanna, was decidedly cool as she headed to the make-up room. In a hurry, we called out our goodbyes in unison. I hung on before shutting the door for Mildred to reciprocate, but I shrugged off her silence and decided she'd probably not heard me.

Suddenly convinced we had thrown away her valuables, read her mail, or worse, pilfered through her pocketbook, Mildred waited for the front door to shut before she entered the living room to search through the rubbish bags awaiting disposal. She sorted through them, retrieving newspapers, a broken lamp, dozens of dirty tissues, enough wooden cocktail sticks to build a replica of the Eiffel Tower, remnants of food, old ripped magazines, and unsolicited junk mail informing Mildred she'd won a prize. All of it was dumped about her recliner when I get home.

'Darling,' said Mildred, facing me as I opened the front door around quarter to five, her hair unkempt, her eyes wild. 'I've got some heavy, heavy stuff going on here, darling. I'm sure I've won millions, this letter says so,' she said, waving one half of a torn letter. 'Now my chance is ruined because that female threw it away! Shit!' she screamed. 'I wanna kill her! These millions are for Baby!'

Her mood left me taken aback. We had had mini tiffs up to now, mostly over Rosebud defecating, but nothing that warranted such rancour.

'Millions!' she cried. 'Baby needs millions!'

I took the letter from her and tossed it onto the sofa. 'This is crazy,' I said angrily, but at the same time trying to remain calm. '"Millions, Baby needs millions" – we're trying to help her, Mildred! If we hadn't blitzed the place, the dirt and germs in here would have bumped you off first.' Mildred hadn't heard me. She was tossing around paper from the larger of the two C&A carrier bags. In a temper, she kicked a Simpson of Piccadilly bag across the living room, which sent Rosebud scampering for the hall. 'I had everything, and Baby will have nothing from me.' Unable to calm her, I gave up and left. Ten minutes later she was knocking on my bedroom door.

'Oh, Orstin, can I come in? Mildred's been a naughty girl,' she enquired. Without waiting for me to answer, she opened the door cautiously. 'Can you forgive little Cissie Shay and please come out to play?'

'Come in, Cissie Shay,' I said from where I was sitting on the bed, my tone still curt. Mildred pushed the door wider. She appeared from behind it, holding a bottle of vodka and two glasses.

'How about we toast your little lady? Wouldn't that be nice, dear?' she said, edging closer. She placed the vodka bottle and glasses on the chest of drawers and poured.

'I hope you mean that,' I said. Mildred crossed her heart. We chinked glasses.

'You won't leave, will you?' she pleaded, polishing off her cocktail. 'I'm sorry, I was so meanie about Joanna. I'm done with being alone,' she said, forlorn. 'I've tasted

51

what it is to have family again. I can't bear the idea of being alone.'

'You were out of order,' I said calmly.

'It's Baby, she worries for her Mama,' said Mildred. 'Don't leave, will you, Orstin?' she begged, changing the focus back to me.

'We're not leaving,' I said, and pulled a tissue from my pocket and handed it to her. I was oblivious to the fact that ultimately one of us would have to walk.

Four

The Dinner Party

My squabble with Mildred (newly nicknamed Cissie) remained unbeknownst to Joanna. I knew that if I told her she'd be hurt and would want to leave the flat for good. Besides, Mildred and I had made up, so there wasn't any point in raking it over with her. What was more, I was still treading on eggshells: Joanna had suggested shortly before we moved in with Mildred that as soon as she finished her school placement, we should relocate to the country: the Forest of Dean to be exact. As I felt my life and career (to use the term loosely) were in London, I was determined to stick it out – tantrums, cat shit, and all.

Joanna would have hated to know Mildred thought ill of her. Joanna was one of the most honest people I knew, second only to Julie, her mother. The truth was, going back over our argument in my mind, Mildred refused to believe that these letters about prize money were a scam, or that the phone calls she received from dubious individuals were a con. Whenever Mildred asked me to post a cheque to one of these unscrupulous companies, I'd lie and say I had posted it, when I'd actually thrown it down the rubbish shoot off the kitchen balcony.

* * *

Before I'd approached Mildred with the suggestion of our lodging with her temporarily, my brother Howard had said we could stay with him for a bit, in his large split-level three-bedroom rented flat at the Oval, Kennington. However, his two existing flatmates had certainly never shown any sign they'd welcome guests. Perhaps Meredythe might have, at a push, but definitely not Ian; he couldn't so much as crack a smile in my presence. When I did occasionally stay over, Ian would leave the same laminated note that read 'DON'T TOUCH MY DECKS' propped up on the mantelpiece in the living room.

It surprised me that the all-but-mute Ian would think I'd want to take a spin on his 'wheels of steel', in the corner of the room covered by Laura Ashley curtain fabric, which I felt was quite at odds with the records stacked next to them: American hip-hop, Beastie Boys, Tribe Called Quest, and *Smack My Bitch Up* by The Prodigy. The note irritated me. How I'd have loved to pull a wire. Joanna thought Ian peculiar, but it was Mildred who offered the most vocal opinion.

We had been in our 'flat share' for just over a month when I announced to Mildred over breakfast that Howard had invited us to his flat for dinner that coming Saturday. I had to repeat myself three times. Joanna noticed that it wasn't that Mildred hadn't heard; more that she was so excited to have been invited out that she could hardly comprehend the idea.

Convinced she'd heard Kensington and not Kennington, Mildred couldn't help elevating Howard, and by association herself, to a swankier stratosphere.

Within minutes I heard Mildred on the telephone to Lady Janet: 'Well, of course, Janet, dear, it may just be an intimate dinner, but I'm sure he'll invite his Kensington Garden neighbours – you know of course Geoffrey and I were chummy with Princess Marina of Greece? No? Oh, my dear, we would go for cocktails at the Palace all the time.'

If the offer wasn't enough, my mention that Howard was unattached trumped whatever else might have been on the menu. If Mildred couldn't have me, she'd happily settle for 'the brother,' her pet name for Howard – for now, anyway.

'Oh, Orstin,' called Mildred, when our dinner date was just two days away. 'Orstin, dear, I've telephoned Lady Davidson. I can't say I like her very much, but darling, she always looks the part, so I asked the name of her hairdresser.'

'Oh, that's good, Cissie,' I answered as I grabbed my coat and bag, preparing to head out the door. I was surprised she'd thought about venturing out, but I smiled, as I was certain she was aiming to impress my brother.

'Oh, Orstin,' she continued, 'Get this, she has a female do her hair, for Christ's sake!'

I detected more grumblings as I grabbed the packed lunch Joanna had made for me from the fridge.

'Are you still there, Orstin?' Mildred asked.

'Just!' I said, standing in the doorway to the living room, bag in hand, my coat over my arm.

'Orstin, darling, can you call British Telecom and find out if that Italian fella 'Mister Itsy Bitsy'…no, wait a minute…Itsy Bitsy Raymond is still in business, will you, dear?' she said. 'Oh, Gawd, the very idea of a female creeping all over me. Oh, Gawd, I wanna be sick.'

'Who?' I asked, sniggering. I had a sudden memory of Howard and I in front of the television, watching novelty-spectacle-wearing children's presenter Timmy Mallet singing *Itsy Bitsy Teenie Weenie Yellow Polkadot Bikini*, back in what I thought was the 1980s, on the kids' show *Wacaday*. 'Are you sure you've got that right?' I asked again, laughing loudly as I attempted to sing the song.

'Oh, darling, oh, now listen, I know that tune,' she said, joining in laughing with me as she got to her feet. My coat dumped on the floor, I stabilised her as we proceeded to jig about the living room, with only Rosebud there to witness the spectacle of us dancing and my singing. With no puff left, Mildred flopped back into the recliner.

'Oh, shit!' she cried. 'I've just realised, that's not his name at all! His name was Teasie Weasie! Oh, Gawd,' she roared. 'I'm a dumb broad, but honestly, I've not danced like that since I did that pop video,' she said, breathless. (I never fathomed which pop video she referred to.)

'Oh, yes, Teasie Weasie. He's a big deal, darling. He has that place in Soho I go to,' she said.

(Judging by her unkempt bottle-blonde coiffure, the jury was out as to whether Mildred had been to see Itsy Bitsy, Teasie Weasie, or any suchlike in quite a while.)

'Oh, I had his card someplace...' She looked in a bulging letter-rack on a table beside the recliner. 'I'm sure your 'wifie' must have tossed it out during the spring clean,' she moaned as she rummaged.

Deciding not to spoil the fun, and definitely not wishing to open that wound again, I simply agreed to check. As it turned out, Teasie Weasie – or giving him his proper title, Raymond Bessone OBE – had been a celebrated hairstylist. However, as with most of those Mildred counted as 'darling' friends, Raymond had been retired since the sixties and dead since the nineties.

Mildred had mentioned Leonard of Mayfair, who unlike Raymond was still alive, but very much retired. Vidal Sassoon, who'd trained under Teasie Weasie, was deemed off-limits. I automatically thought it was because of the cost of a Sassoon haircut; however, Mildred seemed to recall they'd had an 'affair' once, after his re-popularising of the bob cut, but prior to his creating the pixie cut for Mia Farrow. 'It was the sixties,' she said. 'I was a swingin' chick!' She corrected herself, hands on hips: 'I am still a swingin' chick!'

Mildred finally knuckled under and allowed Lady Davidson to book her in to see Michelle Jones on the King's Road at eleven the next morning.

* * *

I was vaguely aware of Mildred up and about. It had to be early. As it was Saturday morning, we were happily in bed. I felt myself doze. I was woken by a knock at our bedroom door.

'Oh, children,' Mildred cried, 'it's Cissie Shay!'

'What time is it?' moaned Joanna in my ear, barely able to muster a whisper from under the duvet.

I'd no idea – still dark.

'Oh, Orstin!' Mildred called louder. 'I hope you're not decent!' There was a snigger as the door crept open. 'Now you kids stay doing whatever I wish I were doing. I just wanna look inside my wardrobes.'

Our room had a bank of built-in floor-to-ceiling wardrobes, four double-width cupboards in a row. Inside there was barely room for either Joanna or me to hang a T-shirt.

Mildred had awoken at five, her thoughts on what she'd wear to Howard's tonight. She told us as we lay with the duvet all but over our heads that she'd remembered she'd got clothes in our room.

With one eye open, I peered at the apparition before me in an off-white (more sour milk-yellow) lace nighty. I detected an odour too: a pungent cocktail of Giorgio Beverly Hills perfume and Elnet hairspray applied undoubtedly for my benefit.

'I haven't looked inside those wardrobes in years...Oh, boy, now Joanna's gonna love my gowns,' Mildred said excitedly. I sat up for the presentation.

Mildred flung open the nearest sliding wardrobe door, metal screeching across rusty casters. 'Now you're talking. I gotta show you my gowns – my clothes cost millions...you'll never have seen anything like it, especially being from the countryside. I have an Adrian in there.' Joanna didn't attempt to move – his name meant nothing to her.

With Joanna and I tucked up, Mildred talked of Adrian's status at MGM. The man who had created Dorothy Gale's ruby slippers for *The Wizard of Oz* was a firm friend. He had never made a pass – happy as he was in his lavender marriage to the butch Janet Gaynor. I felt the weight of clothes on my feet as Mildred yanked one coat hanger after the next from the wardrobe, and tossed them onto the bed. The bottom half of the bed was piled high with a colourful jumble.

Joanna threw back the duvet and stomped from the room. Mildred was too engrossed to notice she had gone. In fact, she was certain Joanna was there, as it was obviously for her benefit and not mine that Mildred's commentary continued.

Joanna reappeared a few minutes later. 'It's early, Mildred,' she said as she rubbed her eyes. 'I'd like a lie-in.'

Mildred pulled out a black dress with a shell-pink under-skirt and held it up against Joanna. 'Oh, now you have a figure, darling. You should try it. Wait, I have the shoes too. What size are you?'

'I'm a five,' said Joanna, as she stood in her PJs with her arms crossed while Mildred delved deeper into the wardrobes.

'Oh, shame,' said Mildred, looking Joanna up and down. 'That's big, dear.' Without looking, Mildred tossed the Adrian onto the bed. 'Try it on later, darling, I've gotta find my…Oh, now, I know you're in here someplace,' said Mildred, her head so deep inside the wardrobe that she was only visible from the waist down. I was out of bed too at this point. Joanna pointed to my boxers and mouthed, 'Put some clothes on.' I did as she said and grabbed my Levi's from the floor.

Mildred backed out of the wardrobe, a dress in either hand. She had found her Paquin and her Pucci. The latter was multi-coloured pink, emerald green, caramel and chocolate – the colours shouldn't work, but they did somehow. Grabbing a bird of paradise hat from a box by her feet, Mildred continued to put on a show, with tales of how the Queen Mother marvelled at her every Ascot Ladies' Day.

With Joanna's enthusiasm growing, Mildred became even more animated, and while the Paquin and Pucci joined the Adrian on the bed, Mildred yanked out a navy blue strapless gown by Balenciaga, followed by a mauve jersey Jean Muir.

Next to come out of the closet was a bitter chocolate suit jacket and a tweed two-piece. Both bore the label Hardy Amies. Mildred egged on Joanna to try on the tweed and helped her into it.

'Oh, now, don't you look wonderful, Joanna!' said Mildred as she admired her.

'You really do Joanie,' I said, joining in.

As Mildred told it, Hardy Amies was a dear friend to whom she had been introduced by her actress-turned-aristocrat friend Virginia Cherill, Countess of Jersey, and her American chum, Mrs Dickie Gleeson.

Mildred now sat amongst her clothes on the bed. She described how she and Geoffrey had been living at the Beverly Wilshire Hotel in two suites paid for by Joseph A. Shay, when in 1940 Geoffrey decided he wanted to return to his home country and 'do his bit' for the war effort. Mildred contacted Hardy well in advance so that he would be well-prepared. She knew Britain was in the thick of it, so didn't want Hardy to create anything too fussy for her. She therefore agreed on a suit using Linton fabrics.

'Because I was coming from Hollywood, Hardy decided it would be rather fun to leave the salvage 'Made in England' and use this to edge the lapels as decoration,' she said.

The couple's journey hadn't been an easy one. Unable to find passage, the pair had to make do crossing the Atlantic on a 700-tonne Norwegian freighter. Both were given roles to perform, with Mildred, the only woman on board, trained to man the Oerlikon gun.

She writhed around on the bed as she remembered life on the ocean waves. She had been bestowed with the luxury of a cabin boy, whom she had entrusted with her Max Factor make-up box. It had been fit to burst with lipsticks, powders, and potions, but underneath all that there had been a hidden compartment to store her jewellery and platinum cigarette holder.

She told us that she had given the cabin boy precise instructions that, should they be torpedoed, he should grab the box and her mink, and if possible her sable, and should there be time, her silver fox too. She had slept in the Made in England suit with her shoes on, fully made-up.

Every morning her young servant had brought her a jug of hot water.

She joked with Joanna and I that there had been enough water to wash as far as possible – and her 'possible'.

Mildred noticed I wasn't laughing.

'My possible! My beaver!' she roared, pointing at her crotch.

By the time the freighter had arrived in Scotland,

Mildred had reckoned she was the best-known person on board and played with the seamen. 'On the final night of the voyage I put on a helluva show,' she said, up on her feet. 'The boys wept.'

'I bet you reminded them of their mothers,' said Joanna with a snigger.

'Oh, honey, I reminded them what they'd been missin'.'

Things had been more refined when she had reached London. While standing at the window, Mildred looked out over the city and told us how Geoffrey had been whisked away on a special operation given to him by Winston Churchill, and so she installed herself at the London Savoy. 'It was full of Americans,' she said. Sir Hugh Wontner, Managing Director of the Savoy Hotel Group, had made sure she was well looked after. 'I remained holed up in my suite until VE Day,' she said.

'How glamorous,' said Joanna. She was intrigued by a second colourful Pucci dress and held it up to herself.

'Darling girl, I witnessed first-hand what you refer to as the British stiff upper lip!' Mildred said, resting on the foot of our bed again. 'There was an almost direct hit on the Savoy one night as I slept. The windows blew in, and a cold breeze filled my room.' Mildred got to her feet and waved her hands to further illustrate her plight. 'The next morning, after a night in the hotel's marvellously plush air raid shelter, I went down for breakfast. I was flabbergasted to hear an old lady turn to her friend, both drinking tea, the restaurant curtains blowing widely, glass in the sugar bowl, and say, "Now isn't this a lovely cup of tea?" I knew then you British were eccentric at best.'

Mildred recited to us her predicament: often bumping into Churchill and dining on game sent to her by Geoffrey's old nanny, who was living in grace-and-favour apartments within Hampton Court. Mildred's had been a different war to those of my own family members. One of Mildred's greatest horrors was having to dine in the restaurant behind a screen. The maître d' was nervous that fellow diners would get riled up, seeing her tuck into pheasant while they ate toast. On some occasions, Sir Hardy Amies, Lord Mountbatten, and other friends joined her. 'They knew where to find a good square meal – with an imposing five-shilling price tag,' she said with great boastfulness.

'So you weren't on the front line, as it were, Mildred,' I said, as I pulled a sweater from a pile of my own clothes on a chair next to me.

'You kiddin'!' she squealed.

As it turned out, Mildred, inspired by what Hardy Amies told her of his friends in the Belgian Resistance, decided that she too wanted to work undercover. I laughed at the thought that Mildred could have been trusted to keep a secret; what was more, her 'all or nothing' attitude meant she wouldn't consider working in an ammunition factory like my Aunt Peggy, who was rather grand but nevertheless had been happy to muck in. No, Mildred saw herself as Odette Hallowes – anything less would have been too meagre a deal.

'Cecil Madden, a big noise at the BBC, put me off though,' said Mildred, as she toyed with one of her dresses. 'Cecil sat me down and warned me I may have to share dorms and share my comb and toothbrush with other girls, so I decided it wasn't for me.' I wondered if Odette ever wavered in the face of the same predicament.

Instead, Mildred had taken on the role of MC at the Queensbury Club in London, where she had hosted shows for servicemen, engaging such turns as comedian Tommy Trinder, Forces' sweetheart Anne Shelton, and the Dagenham Girl Pipers.

As Joanna helped Mildred by tidying the clothes on the bed, Mildred retrieved her Hardy Amies 'Made in England' jacket. Mildred and Sir Hardy Amies had remained friends. Mildred reckoned she continued to go to his salon shows at the House of Hardy Amies on Savile Row throughout the 1970s and 80s. But by the look of the jumble on the bed, I doubted she had bought anything new after about 1982 – perhaps she just went along for a gossip, found herself a plate of canapés and a glass of champagne, and sandwiched herself between friends Margaret, Duchess of Argyll and Dame Barbara Cartland on the front row.

Mildred handed Joanna the jacket. 'It looks good on you, dear,' Mildred said as she stood before Joanna, fiddling with the collar. Mildred pulled at the sleeve. 'Oh, you should really try it on without that queer bed attire...what are you doing with your hand, dear? Have you found some money in the pocket?' Mildred asked.

'No, it's not money, Mildred, look.' Joanna poked her finger through a large moth hole in the left patch pocket.

'Whatcha say...' Mildred went from elated to

mortified in seconds. 'Oh, no! Oh, I'm a wreck, how did that happen? Oh, Orstin, come and hold me up here! What is it? What is it?'

'Moths, Mildred,' said Joanna.

We were banned from mentioning moths again. With Mildred installed in the recliner, taking puffs from her inhaler, Joanna returned to the bedroom to hang Mildred's clothes back in the wardrobe. It was a tough job: gowns, jackets and dresses were rammed three on a hanger.

I switched on *BBC Breakfast News*. It was only once Dermot Murnaghan had come on screen that Mildred calmed. I left her and headed for the kitchen, where I made her a cup of her favourite Lady Grey tea. She instructed me to add lots of sugar to help with the shock, and 'perhaps a side of brandy, darling'. The latter was out of the question.

Along with a bottle of Warnicks Advocaat and a half-full bottle of Dubonnet, both older than me, Joanna had ditched the dregs of a murky Christopher's Monseigneur Brandy bottle. The label which described it as 'Three Star Quality' had most definitely lost its sparkle.

Mildred passed by me in the hall, and waved away the tea I'd made her. Instead she headed for our bedroom. She clung to the wall in such a way that one would think she'd been shot. Her yelps for help further demonstrated that she'd been severely wounded by the decrepit state of her costumes.

Joanna suggested perhaps she could try and do an invisible mend, or perhaps her own mother Julie could have a go. But Mildred wasn't sure if country folk from the Forest of Dean would be used to handling such exquisite fabric. This got Joanna's back up. She fetched two 'holey' blouses and a pantsuit.

'Mildred,' she said, 'there's nothing exquisite about crimplene.'

Mildred didn't register. She headed to the make-up room, still visibly upset. I thought an application of lipstick was bound to pep her up.

It was only after a Nescafé cappuccino (with a nip of Tia Maria) and three Rennies that Mildred mustered enough courage to re-enter the bedroom. She clung to the door frame. We had both showered and were ready to head out. Joanna, calm again after the 'forest folk' jibe, invited Mildred to join us for a coffee at Starbucks. Mildred declined and disappeared.

She called out for me just as I was pulling on my jacket. I left Joanna at the front door and went back to her recliner.

'Oh, how did this happen to me though? Oh, Orstin, isn't it awful, us being infested.' She turned and looked slowly over her shoulder, her movement calculated, as if a moth larva assassin might just jump out and munch her to death.

Joanna decided we should stay a while. She discarded her coat on the cedar chest in the hall and came back into the living room. Mildred was grateful we had postponed our coffee break. We sat with her as she roared over the volume of the television, and she shared more stories of her life on-board ship.

I wagered it was not the moths that had caused such hysteria, but rather the realisation that the little she had left from her old world was now completely falling apart. I looked towards the dirty window ledge, where photographs of Baby at varying stages of life stared back at me. Perhaps Baby was Mildred's only living reminder of what had once been.

With the *BBC Breakfast* credits rolling, Mildred diagnosed herself as too unwell to watch the cookery show *Saturday Kitchen*. She hated cookery programmes and celebrity chefs – aside from having had a certain liking back in the day for Fanny Craddock. They'd met at Norman Hartnell's Bruton Street salon in Mayfair in the seventies. Mildred liked a woman who wore make-up, and Fanny wore hers in bucket-loads. The only temptation for Mildred on the *Saturday Kitchen* menu nowadays was host James Martin.

With Joanna and I either side of her, and Rosebud in tow, Mildred struggled up from the recliner. We were moving slowly enough that she caught a glimpse of Martin with a large potato masher. 'Now that's a dish I'd like to lick clean,' she said, still well enough to be raunchy.

When Mildred was back in bed she asked that Joanna fetch her the Made in England jacket. Joanna did so, and Mildred put it around her own shoulders. As I fluffed her pillows, she grabbed my arm.

'Oh, no, who could have brought in horrid bugs? Oh, it's awful, oh, I've got it! I bet it's from Re-shit-a.' Mildred's eyes darted towards the window. 'You think she's got something disgusting on her?' she added.

'No, Mildred, the unmentionables like dark undisturbed places,' I said, trying to reassure her.

'Dark! Well, bingo, dear! There you have it – she is dark, and from what she's told me of her sex life with that husband, he's disturbed. She told me his mother was a refugee, and I did once see her in the gardens down below with an older woman, eating on a park bench! Oh, Gawd, you have gotta feel for these poor people, but really my clothes cost millions – millions!' She still had hold of the Amies jacket and picked up her Bible from her bedside table. 'You can't even buy these clothes today.'

Joanna took the jacket and placed it back on a hanger in Mildred's room. All the closets creaked under the weight of clothes.

'You can't be casting aspersions, Mildred,' said Joanna. 'Resheda is here to help you.'

'She is a home hindrance,' barked Mildred.

'Let me fix it for you,' Joanna said, exasperated. She looked at me. 'Hey Austin, haven't you got a suit bag? It will protect these from further damage.'

Mildred grabbed Joanna's elbow. 'Oh, that's marvellous, oh, you sweet child! I love you!' She gave Joanna a kiss – her red lipstick left a mark on Joanna's pale cheek. 'Oh, look, Orstin, that's what she looks like in make-up!' she sniggered.

'I wear make-up, Mildred!' said Joanna. 'I'm just not as obvious as you.'

I sensed things could become heated so I started to guide Joanna from the room just as Rosebud entered. The cat circled and then settled almost under Mildred's chin. Rosebud twitched and started to scratch herself wildly. Joanna motioned to Rosebud and then muttered to me, 'There's the culprit.'

But Rosebud was a house cat. Joanna and I hadn't seen her venture beyond the kitchen balcony, and only once did I see her at the living room window. That had been the day I was astonished to notice a man below in the carpark with a kestrel on his arm. I had pointed him out to Mildred and Joanna. Mildred, in a blind panic, ran for Rosebud, clutching the cat to her bosom. 'Shut the curtains, Orstin! Shut the curtains – the Bud! My Rosie!' she screamed. 'She'll be toast if that cholesterol sees her!' Like Ethel Skinner in *Eastenders*, Mildred often got her words muddled up, with hilarious results.

Considering that she had lived on Ritz crackers and vodka martinis, Mildred was worried that Rosebud didn't eat much. She rebuffed the notion that cats just have a small appetite. Mildred followed Rosebud around the flat and held her dish next to her face, pleading that she eat three square meals a day. When Rosebud declined, as she always did, Mildred tried a new tactic: she chased her about the living room with morsels of sliced ham or chicken on a fork. When this too inevitably failed, Mildred then tossed food at her, which was subsequently left untouched on the carpet. During the great clean-up, Joanna and I found decomposing chunks of Whiskas oozing into the carpet.

Mildred was languishing in bed. I promised to buy some mothballs at Woolworth's whilst we were out. I pulled the door – however, before I closed it fully, I was made to promise we would try an alternative ironmonger. Mildred reminded me that she knew Barbara Hutton, and with all 'the dough' she and the Woolworth clan had amassed, Mildred was determined she'd not give them a penny more. Joanna heard Mildred's orders and called out from the front door that we would try Robert Dyas. Mildred was jubilant: she'd known one of the Dyas family, and considered them to be from good Irish stock and far less showy than Barbara Hutton.

Three hours later we return with moth balls, and wine to take to Howard's. Mildred was up and about in a favourite yellow David Nieper negligee, her hair backcombed, her make-up caked on. On the kitchen door hung the crimplene trousersuit Joanna had located earlier, over which Mildred had tossed her silver-fox wrap.

Joanna and I were delighted that she was calm. I discovered the reason: she had telephoned the doctor's surgery in our absence and, it being a Saturday, left a message on the answerphone asking for someone to call her back urgently. She had wanted to arrange a teta-nus jab, to avoid any illness she might suffer should the moths develop a taste for human flesh and move in on her. Mildred suggested we have a booster each.

'Mildred, it's moths. We won't be contracting malaria,' I said, flabbergasted.

She was not be moved. 'It's alright for you, dear – tall, dark, handsome, and full of throbbing young muscle!' she said as she flopped in the recliner.

Joanna scoffed when later I told her Mildred's flattering description of me. 'Austin,' she said, 'Mildred would go for any man under forty with a pulse.' With that, Joanna headed out the door to meet Kirsty for lunch. I made Mildred and myself sandwiches.

It was not only the vacuum cleaner that was an alien

creature to her. In the time we had lived with Mildred, she hadn't so much dried a cup or wiped a countertop. While we were at Starbucks earlier, Mildred had ventured so far as to rinse out her own underwear: a couple of greying Wonderbras and three thongs were hung from the mixer taps, and dripped into the kitchen sink full of cold water. Her cereal bowl, a plastic beaker, a teacup, and Rosebud's food dish were submerged, while a film of Rosebud's hair and Whiskers leftovers floated on the surface.

So before I tackled the sandwiches, I tackled the sink. I was soon aware that there was someone behind me. I turned to face Mildred, as my hand clutched her brassiere.

'Oh, now, hello boys! she said, hand on hip, and looked at me as she relieved me of her smalls. 'Gawd! The wife's back is turned for just a moment and you're in my B-cups!' She slung the bras over the counter towards the bread bin. They landed with a splat. 'Now you've seen mine, how about you show me yours?' she said and roared with laughter.

I couldn't help but laugh too, although I was aware that I'd turned red. She elbowed me. 'Oh, honey, I'm just awful,' she said, her manner akin to Dick Emery, as she continued to the fridge to retrieve the vodka. With the precision of a skilled barman, she manoeuvred around me as she mixed us each a cocktail. As she made her exit, Mildred warned me that she can't eat lunch. The trauma of earlier had left her without an appetite. I feared for Howard that evening; his culinary expertise might be wasted on Mildred.

I wolfed down a cheese and pickle roll standing up in the kitchen and took just a sip of the martini before I headed out to meet Joanna and Kirsty. I left Mildred in the make-up room. She was preparing for tonight.

Ian had told Howard that he was intrigued to meet Mildred. Howard later heard him describe her to a DJ friend as 'a bona fide Hollywood oldie'. Much to Howard's relief, Ian had also informed him that he wouldn't be staying for dinner. As a vegan, Ian had confided in Howard that he had a hard time cutting the tops off carrots; and as a Marxist, Ian was also not a fan of Howard's rich cooking, nor his elaborate flair for setting a dining table. Ian considered Howard very bourgeois.

Yet it was Ian who answered the door to us with a deadpan 'hello'. Mildred, who herself was wearing a seventies black pant-suit, gold sling-backs, diamond bracelet, earrings, and silver fox, was caught quite off-guard by his get-up – as was Joanna, although Joanna and I had witnessed one or two of his other eccentricities before.

It wasn't Ian's glittery jeans that stunned Mildred, nor even his sweater with George and Zippy from the children's television show *Rainbow* emblazoned across the front, but the hat, a sort of desert combat helmet accessorised with green netting and a giant plastic bug stuck to the front. I did my best to guide her up the stairs from the front door to the living space as quickly as possible, for fear that Mildred would have something not entirely appropriate to say.

Next up was Meredythe, who was wearing lycra. She reached for Ian's hand and told us that they'd just got engaged that morning, and that they'd not be staying for dinner as they were off for a bike ride. I followed Mildred's gaze as she watched the pair head from whence we had come.

'Shit! Get a load of that guy,' said Mildred to me, and her whisper echoed through the flat. 'What's 'the brother' doing living with that weirdo? Oh, Gawd, I'm glad they're not staying to eat, after my morning I can't stand to look at any more bugs. That guy's get-up gives me the creepy-crawlies.'

Joanna started talking loudly to mask Mildred, as she had noticed that Ian and Meredythe were looking back up at us from the foot of the stairs.

'You know what flies eat, don't you?' said Mildred, just as Howard appeared. 'Bugs eat shit!'

Her tone changed when she saw Howard. It was obvious from the get-go that Mildred adored him.

'Well, hello, handsome,' she grinned, newly-applied lipstick smudged across her teeth.

Howard greeted her by kissing her hand as if she were a dowager princess. I wanted to laugh: without question Howard was a more sophisticated version of me, but this took him into a whole new stratosphere. I'd never seen him do this before. Mildred lapped it up.

'Oh, darling, I feel like the Queen of the May.' She looked from Howard to me and back to Howard, and, holding his hand, told him he could teach me a thing or two. 'He can be real rough sometimes,' she giggled. 'Not that I'm complaining!'

'Austin has always been the rebellious twin,' sighed Howard.

She marvelled at the crispness of the table linen, at the cut crystal wine glasses, and fine Spode dinner service inherited from our grandmother Violet. Howard was determined to impress Mildred. She was awestruck.

He wasn't sure quite what to make of her at first, although both Joanna and I had already told him about our new lives with an old star. For one thing, after their initial greeting, Mildred set about making excuses for why she couldn't possibly eat any of his food: that our earlier catastrophe had left her grieving for a 'million dollar wardrobe'. Howard told her not to worry, but I sensed his disappointment – not to mention the expenses he'd gone to in order to impress her.

When Howard was out of the room, I urged Mildred to try at least a morsel of something and suggested that perhaps she might be feeling peculiar because she was hungry.

'Oh, Orstin, and how! I tell ya, I'm hungry for that brother of yours,' she said, and fumbled for a lipstick, eager for his return. 'He reminds me of my beloved Geoffrey.'

Mildred did manage some champagne. According to Mildred, one of her previous doctors at the Belgravia surgery had told her that spatial memory could be vastly improved with the consumption of champagne. After two refills, sitting in a leather armchair in Howard's living room, Mildred explained to Joanna and I that spatial memory was the ability to recognise one's surroundings, as well as perform complex tasks and calculations.

Howard disappeared for another bottle.

'In that case, Cissie, maybe you could undertake the complex task of rinsing the bathroom sink after you've brushed your teeth,' I told her, to which she exclaimed it was difficult to remember to do such menial tasks. I had obviously forgotten that she was the daughter of Joseph A. Shay.

'We had people to rinse sinks,' she said grandly.

'Well, I'm not on your payroll, so it's down to you,' I told her – only half joking.

When Howard reappeared with a fresh bottle, Mildred complained again about how mean I was to her.

'He used to be mean to me, Miss Shay,' said Howard. 'He put roller-skates on me when we were only about eight years old and tied me to the back of his Chopper, leaving me in pieces as he raced off down the street!'

'Oh, boy!' grinned Mildred in my direction, and held her wrists together as if in handcuffs. 'Ooh, baby! Now you're talking!' Her voice was a dead ringer for Mae West. 'I like a chopper, but being tied to one is something I've never done.'

I pretended not to get her innuendo, and proudly announced how she would have marvelled at my shiny red Chopper.

'Well, it's never too late,' she chuckled.

'Oh, God, you two,' said Joanna. 'You're like a couple of *Carry On* characters!'

Howard changed the subject from sex to savouries and offered Mildred a plate of prawn canapés with caviar decoration, and sautéed mushrooms in filo pastry. Her appetite suddenly returned, and Mildred made great headway.

'These are delicious, darling, and Howard – call me Mildred, we're all friends here!'

Despite having said she couldn't eat a thing, Mildred not only polished off the canapés, she also managed a first course of salmon and asparagus terrine, followed by rack of lamb with all the trimmings, chocolate soufflé for dessert, cheese, hand-baked savoury biscuits, coffee, and even strawberries dipped in chocolate. When Howard went out of the room she tipped a dish of After Eights (which Joanna had brought with us as a gift for Howard) into her handbag. Mildred turned her nose up when she noticed Joanna watching her with disapproval. Mildred argued that it was best we take them home.

'That weirdo in the bug-bonnet isn't about to eat chocolate, now, is he?' she said, adding two chocolate-covered strawberries to a napkin that was already home to a lamb cutlet she'd smuggled earlier. She'd caught me staring. This was to be a treat for Rosebud. If we were to feast on riches, so too would her pussycat.

By her own admission, Mildred was 'pissed'. Howard called a taxi, and with him at the front and Joanna and I taking up the rear, we got her down the communal staircase. I propped her up against a bicycle for a moment while Joanna checked to see where the taxi was. Mildred screamed – on the front of the bike was a giant hairy black spider. She was only reassured it was fake after three swipes of her handbag left it motionless. Howard promised her he'd consider giving 'the bug' notice. Mildred had seen both David Hedison and then Jeff Goldblum in *The Fly*, and she was confident there was something alien about Ian, with his eyes too bulbous for her liking.

Back at the flat, Mildred swallowed a handful of aspirin before disrobing. Joanna, playing her dresser, helped her off with the jewellery, the trouser-suit and her bra. Mildred asked that she wait a moment before helping her with her bedwear (another of Baby's purchases: an XXL *Muppet Babies* T-shirt) to admire, just for a moment, her pert bosom.

'What did you say?' I asked Joanna when she was next to me in bed.

'I said she still had a good figure,' said Joanna, snuggled under the duvet.

'What was Mildred's reply?' I asked, surprised. Even for the all-too-often raunchy Mildred, I was truly amazed she had asked such a thing, especially of Joanna.

'Leave it. Let's sleep,' said Joanna.

I sensed she had got a lump in her throat and reached over her for the lamp on her bedside table. 'Hey, what's wrong?' I asked, putting my arm around her.

'She cried,' said Joanna. 'I helped Mildred put on her pyjamas and she cried.'

I lay in the dark, perplexed as to why Mildred would cry. We had had a fun evening and laughed a lot. I decided that she was just drunk, too much champagne, and perhaps she had got sentimental.

It was Lady Janet, Marchioness of Milford Haven, who gave me the answer, much, much later. We had brought youth back into Mildred's life. Joanna and I, and from that evening on Howard too, and soon his friends, and our friends made sure she was having fun.

Mildred didn't want our set-up to end. She couldn't bear the thought of ageing, of becoming a burden, of our leaving and her finding herself back in a place of emptiness and loneliness. It didn't happen. She was almost never alone again.

Five

Thanksgiving

*D*espite the fact that Joanna and I had only been living with Mildred for a short while, she'd mentioned on many occasions that she detested anything remotely associated with hospitals. She wouldn't even tune in to see George Clooney on *ER*, even though she was keen on him, in case there was blood – or worse, death – onscreen.

We were therefore surprised when, one evening as she sat in the recliner with a dinner-tray on her lap, she actually appeared to watch more than a few minutes of the BBC drama *Holby City*. She'd usually turn over just as soon as she saw a white coat; however, from what I could gather as Joanna and I chatted, the storyline had something to do with the after-effects of a botched abortion. This was sustaining her interest.

I was not sure who jumped the highest – Joanna, Rosebud, or me – in reaction to Mildred's sudden outburst of tears, which sent her meal of salmon fishcakes flying. So unexpected, so loud, so shocking was it, that one would have thought Mildred had been shot.

As she sobbed, Joanna knelt on one side of Mildred, and I on the other. We managed to ascertain that her former husband Winthrop, or 'Winnie' as she referred to him, hadn't taken well to the news that he was about to become a father. He had corralled Mildred within their Palm Beach mansion whilst he telephoned her actress friends, Arline Judge and Honeychilde Wilder, insisting he would pay them to come and visit. Once they were there, Winnie had the girls pack Mildred's bags and take her with them back to Hollywood, where they were to introduce her to a nice doctor.

'All I remember was asking for my baby,' sobbed Mildred as she gripped onto Joanna's shoulders.

'Cissie, you're actually hurting me,' said Joanna, and tried to peel Mildred's hands away gently.

'I wanted my baby, I wanted my baby,' she wailed.

Still tearful, she described how her supposed friends had left her bedside immediately after the operation to go to a cocktail party. She told us that Winnie had bedded both Arline and Honeychilde, and eventually dumped Mildred in favour of a Norwegian champion ice skater-turned-movie star, Sonja Henie. Mildred only saw him once after their short-lived marriage ended: 'I was in New York. He approached me on the sidewalk, he asked me to go for a drink. He was drunk, and he was broke too.'

Mildred composed herself and, to Joanna's relief, she pulled away from her – only to cling to me instead. 'I never trusted women again.'

Joanna argued that it was Winnie who was to blame, that Arline and Honeychilde simply danced to his tune.

'Listen, darling,' said Mildred with some force, 'the world needs men.'

There were more fights of this nature to come.

* * *

To lift Mildred's spirits after the *Holby City* episode, we planned a Thanksgiving dinner as a surprise for her. Roast turkey, sweet potatoes, sausage and herb stuffing, cranberry sauce, and a traditional green bean casserole.

I'd rung Mildred's friend in New York, the actress Suzanne Kaaren, a week before to get some menu ideas. I never imagined she was anything like an expert; however, I felt she'd want somehow to be included, even if from afar. Suzanne and Mildred had remained friends ever since they'd worked together on George Cukor's *The Women* in 1939. Suzanne told me what I should serve, and estimated how long each dish needed in the oven. She yearned to be able to join us in London. Her set-up sounded rather like Mildred's had been before Joanna and I moved in. The fact that Suzanne told me she never threw anything away from her sprawling Central Park South apartment, and that she had 'lots of cats', was a clue. Both had once been the toast of Tinseltown. I got the impression that, in old age, both were forgotten and lonely. Both ladies had rich landlords too: for Mildred, the Duke of Westminster; for Suzanne, Donald Trump.

Suzanne flip-flopped between saying how much she liked Trump, and how much she loathed him. Her initial hatred, it seemed from what Mildred told me, dated back to the 1980s when Trump had supposedly tried to uproot and evict Suzanne and fellow residents from their rent-controlled apartment block.

Like her friend, Mildred groaned about her own

devious but handsome landlord. 'You know, the Duke turns my heating off, Suzie,' she'd tell Suzanne during their weekly chats on the phone. 'I sit here freezing my arse off.' Mildred failed to mention that the heating was only switched off in the height of summer – nor did she let on that her rent was, like Suzanne's, peppercorn.

Mildred told me Suzanne had later developed something of a crush on Trump. I could not fathom why, and nor could Mildred. When, a short while later, she spotted a photo of Trump in a copy of *Hello!* Magazine, she pondered aloud why it was that she didn't fancy him. Her conclusion was that after her catastrophic six-month marriage to Winthrop Gardner Junior, she could never trust blonde-haired men again.

I'd hidden the turkey I'd bought the day before Thanksgiving as best I could behind other things in the fridge. Mildred spent little time in the kitchen, let alone looking in the fridge. Her daily lunch of Cup-a-Soup meant that I felt sure our secret wouldn't be rumbled. She'd forgotten it was Thanksgiving, a celebration Mildred had previously told me was something of a favourite with her, whichever side of the Atlantic she was on. She told me how, as a girl, she'd sneak bites from her treasured grandmother's cornbread, dipping torn-off corners into thick bubbling mustard-infused giblet gravy. In womanhood, as an actress, and then a wife and mother, she'd always celebrate with loved ones. Mildred admitted to never having cooked a 'bird' herself. In all honesty, she simply hadn't a clue.

On the theme of poultry, Mildred had told me that back in the late 1970s she was called into an emergency meeting with her bank manager, who abruptly informed her that the Shay fortune was spent. Shell-shocked, she and Geoffrey drifted into the Safeway supermarket on the King's Road. There they purchased a whole raw chicken for lunch. 'Oh, Orstin, when we got it home, darling, we looked at one another. Geoffrey guessed it had to be heated but we hadn't the foggiest idea what was to be done,' she said, straight-faced. 'We made passionate love instead and ate potato crisps.'

I was surprised to hear that Geoffrey wasn't more capable in the domestic sphere. Born in South Africa, a former British Cavalry & Guards officer with the First Royal Dragoons, I would have thought that he'd have been used to mucking in. But Geoffrey seemingly escaped any length of time in the field by becoming ill with bronchial fibrosis. Due to this, he was declared no longer able to partake in any active military service.

When Joanna and I had arrived at Kylestrome House, I had mentioned to Joanna that the oven appeared untouched – in marked contrast to the rest of the flat, it positively sparkled. On closer inspection, this was because it was being used as a sort of storage facility, rather than as a means to cook food. On opening it Joanna discovered two address books, the *Yellow Pages* from 1985, a dog-eared copy of *Burke's Peerage*, and two roll-necks.

The death of Geoffrey and the absence of Baby meant Thanksgiving had become meaningless to Mildred. For a decade or more she had spent it sitting alone, the loneliness punctuated only by a call from her daughter.

But no more: in the words of Bob Dylan (whom

Mildred knew – another surprise), the times they were a-changing.

Joanna and I decided we would just tell Mildred when we saw her in the morning that there was to be a dinner party that night. Jubilant, Mildred forwent Dermot Murnaghan and headed directly to the make-up room. I found her in her bedroom two hours later, dressed in a black evening gown, fixing her hair under a black feathered bird of paradise hat. She remained 'ready for action' all day.

I had booked a day's holiday in order to prepare for the dinner. I'd rung Lady Janet, who thankfully agreed to help me by inviting Mildred to her flat for afternoon tea. Mildred adored her, although whereas Lady Janet just wanted to talk about her cats and Mr Pidge, her pet parrot, Mildred preferred Lady Janet to reminisce about her own past glories: holidaying with Queen Elizabeth and Prince Philip on the Royal Yacht Britannia. Mildred could then pepper her reluctant friend with stories of herself, her sister Adeline, and their beloved Daddy at Ascot or Royal garden parties. Mildred had told me that the Shays *en masse* were always a hit. I cringed whenever Mildred retold the story of the Shays at Balmoral, guests of His Majesty King George and his sister The Princess Royal. As Joseph, Lillian, Mildred, and Adeline stepped from their car (Joseph always travelled with his own car, in 1950 a silver-grey Pontiac), Mildred heard King George's consort, Queen Elizabeth, exclaim to her husband at what Mildred perceived as being an alarming volume: 'Darling! It's the Shays from Hollywood!'

'Somehow she'll try and trump me,' Lady Janet had sighed to me over the phone. 'Somehow she'll have a better story, a juicier tit-bit, a more tantalising and torrid tale than I. I just hope she doesn't go on so about drinkies with Princess Marina of Greece.'

Certain Lady Janet could cope, and with Mildred out the way, I washed and polished Mildred's parents' monogrammed silver cutlery, monogrammed serving trays, and the glass and silver cranberry sauce dishes which Joanna and I had found in a trunk in the hall cupboard during the 'big clean'.

Mildred came back from Lady Janet's but we immediately banished her to our own bedroom to keep the surprise. There she watched *Family Affairs* on a seventies portable TV that I'd requisitioned for us from one of the hall cupboards. The television worked perfectly well with a wire coat hanger thrust in the back as a makeshift aerial. It was a lifeline, especially for Joanna, who could then watch what she wanted to, instead of suffering Mildred's tyranny over the living room TV.

What was still a surprise for Mildred was that Howard, along with our friend Adam and his boyfriend Lee, were to be the night's guests. Howard arrived first. He chatted with a delighted Mildred in our bedroom before he shut her in with a martini and *Emmerdale Farm* to allow him to help by laying the table, starting with a new tablecloth Joanna purchased at the Army and Navy store. He arranged the flowers he'd brought in one of Mildred's favourite crystal vases: the only one that didn't have a crack or chip.

When Adam and Lee were also present Joanna and

I led Mildred, who had added her silver fox to her ensemble, into the living room for the big reveal: the table with steaming hot dishes of vegetables, a roast bird at the helm. Arms aloft, she cried tears of pure joy. Adam steadied her as her head flopped backwards. 'Oh, thank-you, Lord,' she screamed heavenwards. She put her arms around my waist and, with tears rolling down her cheeks, she sobbed. That set off Joanna and me too. I wiped away tears as we all sat down, and I carved.

'Now, children,' said Mildred quietly, 'Let me say a few words...now, wait a minute.' She gathered her thoughts.

'We thank you for the gift of life...
er...For the love of family and friends,
without which there would be no life.
We thank you for the mystery of creation:
for the beauty
that the eye can see,
for the joy
that the ear may hear...

(At this point I pointed to my ear, indicating Mildred's whistling hearing aid; Joanna frowned with disapproval.)

for the unknown
that we cannot behold, filling the universe with wonder,
for the expanse of space
that draws us beyond the definitions of ourselves...

Mildred stopped and looked back at us watching her.

'This next bit is for you, kids,' she said quietly.

for friends
who love us by choice...

Mildred looked up again. 'I think that's about all I can remember, folks.'

Adam and Lee gave her gentle applause. Mildred accepted it with delight.

After the meal, Joanna and I were joined by Lee on the sofa-bed in the living room. Our weight caused the foam sponge to pop out from its base, much to the delight of Rosebud, who played with the coloured foam squares. By contrast, Adam was bolt upright in the library chair, and Howard was equally uncomfortable sitting rigidly on a rickety cane carver.

At the epicentre, Mildred sat in the recliner. She selected that night's entertainment: a VHS recording of director Ken Russell's somewhat exaggerated 1977 tribute to silent movie idol Rudolph Valentino, for which she had joined Rudolf Nureyev in an exotic tango, dressed in an over-the-top costume by 'lovely Kenny's' wife Shirley Russell. Mildred was sure 'the boys' would adore her performance and 'just pant for Nureyev,' just as much as she had back then – and now, as she watched herself ham it up on camera.

Mildred was in charge of the TV remote and rewound her small scene three times just in case tonight's audience missed Mildred's two minutes of screen splendour. On each replay, Mildred recounted different romantic moments she had enjoyed in the arms of Nureyev. 'Gay or not, he had the hots for me, and I for him.' She sighed at the remembrance. Her lasting and oft-repeated memory was that there had been something of an intimate moment in the mens' toilet – without a doubt this was hugely exaggerated.

Adam, Lee, and Joanna declined a further replay of *Valentino*, and, each checking their watch, decided it was far too late in the evening to witness Mildred's show-girl routine opposite Alan Ladd in *In Old Missouri* (1939).

Leaving Lee and Howard, Adam helped Joanna and I with the washing-up. Mildred was calling me. She'd relocated to her bedroom.

Adam called for Lee to help him with the rest of the dishes and I handed him a stack of plates to dry as I exited. I wiped my wet hands on a small towel and with it still in my hand, I went in to her. Mildred was sitting on her bed. Gone was the evening dress, and on instead was a pair of candy-pink pajamas that Joanna had bought for her from New Look.

'Orstin, I need to tell you something.'

'Okay, Mildred,' I joked, still holding the towel. 'You're going to say how marvellous an actress you are.'

'No, this is heavy-heavy stuff, Orstin,' she said in all seriousness. 'I want you to know how much I love you,' she said. 'You've no idea what you've done, have you?' I stood before her and shook my head. I gave her a puzzled look and smile. Mildred's face was somber. She handed me a cloth book with an illustration of a boy on the cover. The pages were coloured but faded with age.

'Darling, this was my dear baby brother Arnold's book.' She read me the German title: *Das tapfere Schneiderlein* (*The Brave Little Tailor*). She told me it was Arnold's favourite fairytale and now it was her only memento of him.

'Orstin, if Arnold was alive today I'd have prayed he'd look like you: tall and lean with those lovely sage-green eyes. And be as kind as you are and as loving towards me. I want you to have it,' she said.

I put the towel down on Mildred's chest of drawers. I declined. I felt I couldn't take something with such sentimental value. But Mildred wouldn't have it. The book was passed between us.

'You have no choice,' said Mildred. I knelt down and kissed her, and she held me tight. 'I love you, Orstin,' she said. 'You are my dream of what Arnold could have been.' She kissed me. 'I never wanted a husband when I was young – I wanted my brother, I wanted his protection and his love. I wanted him back because without Arnold our house became a very dark and depressing place.' She told me that their mother had worn black for a decade after Arnold was hit by the car. When Mildred's baby sister Adeline came along, Lillian wrapped her so tightly in metaphorical cotton wool that Adeline was almost never allowed out. She had not been permitted to marry until the age of forty-something, when Adeline finally convinced Lillian that she could be married and still live with her mother. According to Mildred, Adeline had still been a virgin when she married Texan businessman Cal Parker. Finally, Mildred stammered out something that I sensed she had wanted to tell me for some time: that her mother had once said that she'd wished it was Mildred who had died instead of Arnold. Lillian and Adeline had thought that Mildred was 'a Hollywood whore' and had called her as much during heated arguments.

I took the book into the little bedroom and, as I turned the pages, I cried at both Mildred's loss and at my gain.

As I looked at the cloth book, I felt as though I hadn't done anything out of the ordinary to warrant such a prize possession; yet I, of course, realised I was making Mildred happy. It would be all too easy to say, 'Oh, Mildred, it's nothing,' but it wasn't nothing. Joanna and my being there meant everything to her, and as the clock ticked towards December and Christmas, the end of one year and the beginning of another, Mildred was increasingly becoming everything to us.

Though I detected Mildred's unmistakable laughter from the living room and heard it reciprocated by the others, I remained on our bed, clutching Arnold's cloth covered book. I was aware that I was drunk and feeling sentimental, and I took the book, poured myself another glass of wine, and walked out onto the kitchen balcony. I stared out into the darkness and whispered, 'Arnold, she's happy.'

Mildred revealed sometime later that she'd seen a vision of Arnold made flesh again that night during Thanksgiving: standing beside the fireplace as we all sat laughing and joking at the table. It was his idea, she said later, that I have his precious book.

She'd not seen the last of Arnold.

Six

Political Correctness

T he roles had been set: Joanna and I were now cooks, cleaners, cherished companions, and flatmates. Mildred quickly grew to depend on us for everything. One month had turned into more, and there was no immediate plan on anyone's part to change the arrangement.

Once we had left the flat on weekday mornings, Mildred changed from her night attire directly into proper day clothes – the sexy David Nieper nighties no longer formed part of her day, unless she felt unwell. A terrible hypochondriac, she had the Belgravia doctor's surgery on speed-dial. On the occasion of a visit from the doctor, she'd don a David Nieper number and lie in wait in the recliner, adamant that the young handsome locums at the surgery expected movie stars to dress a certain way. She played the dying swan with aplomb.

We had noticed early on that one of her best tricks to fill the void of loneliness was to feign illness – or rather, to genuinely convince herself that she had some terrible affliction; often life-threatening.

It was a common occurrence for me to stay with her until her doctor – or in most cases, a locum from the Belgravia Surgery – arrived to see the patient. In preparation, Joanna had bought a bright red bucket from

Argos, which we left at her side when she wailed that she might be sick. Before then, we had seen her use her cut-glass fruit bowl. Mildred hadn't even considered it unhygienic.

On this particular occasion, I opened the door to a twenty-something female GP and showed her to the living room, where the patient sat whimpering behind a fresh application of lipstick and enormous Sunnie Mann dark glasses. I chuckled as I witnessed her further distress when Mildred saw not Dr Ewan Thomas, a handsome Welshman, but a rotund woman instead. I stayed long enough that I saw the locum take Mildred's pulse and that I heard Mildred ask if the doctor had ever thought of wearing her hair off her face, or perhaps some lipstick.

'Give it to me straight, Doc – am I dying?' I heard her cry as I was closing the front door behind me.

'Yes, Miss Shay,' barked the doctor. 'From your notes, I see you've been dying since your first doctor joined the surgery in 1977.'

Mrs Patel at the pharmacy on Elizabeth Street, where Mildred went for her drugs, told me Mildred drove everyone at the surgery mad. 'She's outlived three of her doctors,' she said.

* * *

On Saturday mornings, while Mildred watched television, Joanna smuggled the clothes Mildred wore the week before out of her wardrobe, added them to our own laundry, and took them, along with a good book, to the local launderette. Joanna piled the clothes into a brown leatherette shopping trolley which we had located in the make-up room. Mildred had been delighted to see the trolley. Referred to now as 'an old friend', she was even more thrilled to see its contents, previously lost to her for a decade or more: three mustard-coloured hand towels, a hat to match her Made in England suit, a couple of Dior scarves, and a black afro wig. It was the latter that brought Mildred most pleasure.

Once one of America's richest, Mildred had adopted a 'Make Do and Mend' mentality. She occasionally chose to wear the wig in the shower instead of 'expensive' shower caps. On one memorable occasion, she'd forgotten it was behind the shower curtain, and with Joanna and I already out for work, she had panicked when she saw it. She called Larry, convinced a giant tarantula had escaped London Zoo and was hiding in her bathroom. She'd often leave it on the ledge of the shower tray to raise a laugh. More than once she walked in on me in the bathroom, wearing only boxers, bent double over the basin, ringing the thing out.

'Darling,' she said to me later, 'I hadn't imagined you were quite so hirsute down there!'

The soggy curly mop was eventually 'lost' down the rubbish chute. When Mildred enquired after it, I told her that I saw Rosebud making out with it in the kitchen, and that she'd probably tossed it over the balcony in a fit of passion. Mildred was sad to learn it was gone, as it had been a gift from Groucho Marx. She recalled how Groucho had chased Mildred around Hollywood, determined she join their act. Mildred had remained steadfast. She was a serious actress and no comedienne. Turning down the Marx Brothers had become another of her great regrets.

She was at least happy that Rosebud had got a thrill out of playing with it. 'Oh, Gawd,' laughed Mildred, 'perhaps Rosie thought it was a big black tom!' She sniggered. 'That's one place her Mama ain't never been.' She turned to me, her look puzzled. 'At least I don't think I have?'

* * *

Despite remaining resolutely in the recliner at meal times, Mildred had begun to share menu ideas for the week ahead. Every suggestion, once cooked and served, was met with new vigour. Mildred's previous diet of vodka martinis, Ritz crackers, and the occasional ready meal delivered from Mr Ali's convenience store had withered her frame to only seventy-five pounds. With a more nourishing diet and, above all, company, Mildred had taken on a new lease of life – and gained a new dress size. There were daily whimpers from the bathroom as she teetered over the scales. 'Oh, Gawd,' she often shouted, 'I've gotten so fat.'

Joanna was usually home first, dumping her bags and then taking the leatherette trolley to fetch food from Sainsbury's. I often joined her there and helped bring the shopping home. Tonight I headed straight for the flat and tossed my bag aside. The door to the living room was open, and the recliner uninhabited. To my surprise, I heard Mildred rattling around in the kitchen.

I surprised her as I entered, since, not being at her usual vantage point, she'd not seen me come through the front door. Mildred was busy: I saw her whisking something.

She laughed when I pretended to faint at finding her in such an alien environment. She hooted as she removed her apron, a gift we had purchased for her at British Home Stores. It was something of a joke really: so many frills and so much froth that it could have been from Fanny Craddock's own wardrobe. Up until this point I'd only seen her wear it over her nightwear. She smiled broadly as she removed it, and took a bow to reveal today's get-up: cut-off Wrangler jeans, off-white blouse tied at the waist, showing her bare midriff, open-toe rattan wedges with her toes spilling from the front, and a colourful scarf that she had fashioned into a turban. Mildred told me she'd watched her old friend Lana Turner as Cora Smith in *The Postman Always Rings Twice* that afternoon on Channel 4, and had felt inspired.

Mildred was proud of her sweet offering, a sort of trifle colliding with a fruit salad. She held aloft the cut-glass fruit bowl before me. There was a slight lurch in my stomach as I recalled what the bowl had previously been used for.

'Welcome home, dear,' she said. 'Mama's been a busy girl.'

'What is it?' I asked, peering in.

Cissie Shay's Surprise, as she had named it, turned out not to be too much of a revelation. Tinned mandarins and sliced oranges (with the skins still attached) immersed in vodka, with a can of Carnation evaporated

95

milk poured in, topped off with maraschino cocktail cherries – one of the only survivors from Joanna's cull of the cocktail cabinet. Mildred looked down on her creation: the milk had curdled with the juice from the fruit. Orange pips bobbed on the surface.

'Well, you're no James Martin,' I joked. I took the bowl from her and covered it in cling-film, then placed it in the fridge. Mildred fiddled with the knot of her blouse and played at being a naughty girl.

'Oh, Daddy,' she said, laughing, 'I did my best.' She wiped her hands on the tea towel, then grabbed a vodka bottle from the countertop and two martini glasses. One had lipstick around the rim. Judging by her wobbly gait, the bar had been open a while.

Joanna declined a drink when she got home thirty minutes later, laden with shopping. She wandered into the living room, where I was sitting with Mildred with the television on but muted. Watching *The Postman Always Rings Twice* and adopting Lana's look had rekindled a memory of an affair Mildred had once enjoyed with John Garfield. There was evidence of their friendship in the photographs in the hall – her 'Rogues Gallery'. The largest and most prominent photograph of the two of them showed Mildred dressed in her Hardy Amies Made in England suit, with Geoffrey in his army uniform, along with the actress Geraldine Fitzgerald. It was dated 1944.

Joanna greeted Mildred with a kiss and then left when Mildred launched into a story of several passionate rendezvous with John Garfield: the two of them 'at it' while Geoffrey was paying visits to Mexican actress

Lupe Velez at her mansion at 732 North Rodeo Drive. Dubbed 'The Mexican Spitfire,' flaming Lupe first met Geoffrey in 1939 at the Cocoanut Grove, when she was fresh from a divorce from Johnny Weissmuller. At the very same moment, Weissmuller had been trying to coax Mildred into having sex with him in the back of his car at Lovers Lookout off Mulholland Drive.

Mildred had thought John Garfield 'a dish'. As with Geoffrey, John Garfield liked a strenuous game of tennis and had a dynamic sex drive. Despite his prowess, the stumbling block for Mildred was, firstly, Garfield's height (just five foot five in his socked feet), and secondly, the fact that she was married.

'Our affair never materialised into anything beyond the odd fuck,' said Mildred, who roared with laughter as she recounted their tumbles between the sheets. 'He was a big boy for a short-arse!'

Mildred quietened her voice as further thoughts of Garfield came flooding back to her. One far less pleasurable event occurred long after they'd gone their separate ways. This time, her father Joseph A. Shay had become embroiled. He'd heard rumours from movie mogul Jack Warner about his daughter's 'friendship' with Garfield, just prior to the latter testifying as a 'cooperative witness' in front of the House Un-American Activities Committee during the anti-Communist witch hunt, which in 1951 was rocking Hollywood to its very foundations.

Sitting back in the recliner, Mildred remembered how her beloved Daddy's place at the heart of the American justice system saved her from being drawn into anything that might have branded her as a Red.

Back in the living room, emptying her school bag onto the dining table, Joanna showed interest in this part of the story – the McCarthy era. She quizzed Mildred on being in Hollywood at that time. Mildred's memories of her fellow Americans fearing 'The Red Menace' were patchy, although she told Joanna and I of an argument with Ginger Rogers' right-wing mother, Leila, whom Mildred knew from her and Ginger's time rooming together at The Garden of Allah.

'Joanna, dear, I can't stand injustice,' said Mildred, polishing off her drink. 'Leila Rogers was wrong: Johnny Garfield was no Red, and he wasn't a darn Pink either, nor an insubordinate! He was no Commie. The Commies I met had close-set eyes – Johnny had real sexy eyes!' she said loudly. 'He loved his country, just as I do.'

Mildred's glass toppled as she kicked back the footrest on the recliner to stand up, albeit precariously, and give the salute. Joanna held her up straight. Mildred's performance ended when she noticed the opening credits for *Eastenders* were rolling on the television. She grabbed the remote from her side table and switched on the volume. She yelled to us that she promised to tell us more after she had watched her show and then flopped back down onto the recliner.

When *Eastenders* had finished, Mildred wandered into the kitchen. She was hungry and blamed her increased appetite to having gone over raunchy memories of boyfriends past.

Mildred caught Joanna taking a gulp from a beer bottle. She scolded Joanna and told her that the sort of people who worked in bottle factories were the types who probably don't wash their hands after they'd used the bathroom. Joanna retorted by asking if these same people were the types who let their pets defecate in their flat. Rosebud had left two deposits, one in the hall outside the bedroom door and another in the living room, only that morning. Joanna had told me she was going to let the issue go; however, Mildred had pissed her off.

It had annoyed Joanna that Mildred supposedly hadn't noticed the cat shit and had let the deposits fester as she sat in the recliner awaiting Dermot Murnaghan – leaving Joanna, as the next out of bed, to clean it up.

With hand on hip, Mildred repeated how fussy her pussycat was, and how if there was a whiff of anything nasty, then Rosebud refused to use her own 'bathroom'. But the cat litter tray was clean. Joanna was adamant instead that Rosebud, like Mildred, wasn't keen on other women. I wasn't sure. I knew from my own scars that Rosebud was definitely not keen on men either – or not on me, anyway.

The dust settled, but only for a moment. Soon we heard Mildred, obviously still sulking, shout from the make-up room that she was thinking about going on a diet, so didn't want whatever Joanna had cooked for that evening after all. I heard this from the living room and confronted Mildred. She'd not be moved – for the moment.

* * *

One of the reasons why Mildred was so afraid of her own appetite was that her mother had instilled in

99

Mildred a terror of putting on weight. Mildred recalled how Lillian would ridicule people who were on the heavier side. Lillian believed the Shays' neighbours in Cedarhurst were obviously from bad breeding stock because of their weight.

'She called the female of the household a 'big black mama', in reference to her weight and tanned skin,' said Mildred a few days later while she applied more lipstick.

Mildred continued, describing how her mother thought it common to sit in the sun. 'She simply couldn't fathom why respectable women would want to colour themselves to resemble Negroes,' said Mildred, as she waved an eye-liner pencil wildly. She continued to refer to the black people from her youth as 'coloured' or 'Negroes'. I heard Joanna slamming about in the kitchen and sensed another argument brewing.

'Are you in there, Joanna?' screeched Mildred. 'Orstin, is Joanna in the kitchen? For Christ's sake…'

'If you two don't stop, I'm leaving,' I shouted at one and then the other of them.

Mildred tossed her hairbrush and came into the kitchen for her martini glass. She downed the remains.

Surprisingly, Mildred calmed down. 'Let's not spoil things,' she pleaded, placing her arms around Joanna, who remained cold as she cut portions of lasagna from a serving dish. Mildred reached around her, took the knife from her hand and laid it on the counter.

'Honey,' Mildred said, 'I'm unarmed.'

Mildred passed Joanna a tumbler for her beer and then rested on the new wooden bar stool. We had bought it in order to coax her into doing the washing-up, with the hope that if she could sit she would clean her dishes. Mildred loved the bar stool but she still didn't wash up.

She reached for Joanna's hand and asked that she leave the food for a moment while Mildred shared some important information.

'Okay,' barked Joanna, her arms crossed. 'And Austin,' she added, 'stop being so passive!'

'Enough!' shouted Mildred, taking both our hands in hers.

'Darlings,' she said, 'didn't I tell you already of my maid Precious, and witnessing nasty racism from even our own President Wilson? We called them Negroes and coloureds. We didn't know any different.' Her voice was apologetic. 'If I worked really hard at home – perhaps walking miles around our estate in West Palm Beach, cutting fresh flowers for the table – Mother would say, "Oh, Mildred, look at you perspiring! Why you've been working like a black!"'

'Oh, for goodness' sake…' said Joanna.

I cut Joanna off. 'For God's sake, Jo, it was a different time,' I said sternly. I also suggested we eat. Mildred wiggled to the recliner while I helped Joanna with the food. Joanna was muttering under her breath all the while.

There were further revelations. After a pudding of spotted dick and custard, Joanna retreated to our bedroom. I sat with Mildred, intermittently checking on Joanna. She was on the phone to her mother, a sure sign that she was not happy. I left them to it.

Sitting opposite me in the library chair, Mildred

confided in me that she felt that perhaps Joanna, being a country girl, lacked worldly knowledge, especially in regard to American history. I started to defend her; however, battling against the volume of the television and having to keep repeating myself, I decided this wasn't a battle I wished to fight right now. Instead, I sat at the dining table and wrote notes for an obituary I was writing.

Mildred was surprised to notice me there thirty minutes later, as she'd been certain I'd left her for Joanna. Mildred had obviously been thinking. She apologised, and listed all the things she felt Joanna excelled at: cooking and cleaning and shopping...Mildred meant well.

'I can tell you how much I like coloured people...' she continued as she pulled out a dining chair and sat next to me. 'Black persons,' she corrected herself. She picked up and read my notes. She recognised the name of the black actress Butterfly McQueen, who was Prissy in *Gone with the Wind*.

'I knew her and I liked her,' she said. '"Queenie" was in *The Women* with me. And Nat King Cole was a dear, dear friend. Geoffrey and I adored him. He sang to me and I to him,' she said, as her eyes welled up at the memory. 'And do you know what I said to him?' she asked forcefully. 'I said he'd the right to make it big, black or not, and we shared a cigarette. I shared his cigarettes, so I wasn't and I'm not racist at all. I was a groundbreaker...' She drifted over to the recliner.

'That girlfriend is very darling to me and so kind, but

honestly, she's a country girl at heart, Orstin. You and I are different class of people.'

* * *

Without any doubt, the biggest shift in Mildred Shay's life was Howard's interest in her. If my role – and most definitely Joanna's – were domestic ones, then Mildred absolutely saw Howard's role as a more public one. His flair for PR-ing Mildred over that first week, having taken her out of the flat and into London's nightlife, had advanced him to her No. 1 spot. Throughout the swing of the pre-Christmas party season, when Howard was not seated opposite her in the flat soaking up her Hollywood stories, he was sharing them and her with others. Billed as a real-life relic from the Golden Age of Hollywood, Mildred had a new, mostly gay, and almost always adoring audience.

After a succession of conversations with his contacts in the fashion press, Howard had wangled Mildred as his plus one to a gallery opening, a dinner with a former Bond girl, and cocktails at a shop launch headed by PR guru Martine Montgomery.

Each time, he obtained a blank invitation and then inscribed Mildred's name in his exquisite penmanship. On receiving them, Mildred was convinced that she hadn't been forgotten after all. The invitations were soon jostling for space on the mantelpiece.

And so it was that, after her decade-long self-exile as Mrs Geoffrey Steele, the widow of a Cavalry and

Guards Officer, Hollywood's Pocket Venus was rising again.

Whereas before she had always been the first up in the morning, at this point Joanna and I would often leave for work with Mildred still in her darkened room, hair in rollers and eye-mask on, as she slept off the night before. Rosebud pawed the carpet, befuddled as to why her 'Mama' wasn't awake.

I arrived home earlier than usual on one occasion. The door to the living room was wide open, the recliner vacant. Having detected the sound of the front door closing, Mildred called out to me from the make-up room. She asked that we left her evening meal on a plate in the fridge, so she could eat it tomorrow for lunch. Instead of her soaps blaring from the TV, she had music playing: her cassette tapes of Nat King Cole, Tony Bennett, and her pop star son-in-law, Gordon Waller. The scene was akin to a teenager preparing herself for a night on the tiles, with Joanna and I in the role of the parents.

She was sitting at the dressing table, facing the mirror. Ken, Joanna's dad, had found new light bulbs at Vivian Carpenters, his local DIY shop in the Forest of Dean. The fifteen working bulbs, plus the overhead light and a table lamp, positively set the room ablaze. So at first, I wondered if it was the extreme lighting that had given Mildred's face an orange glow; however, I soon realised it wasn't that at all, and yet certainly there was something artificial about her. I reached for a tin of Max Factor pan-stick.

'Cissie,' I said, 'I think you've gone too heavy with the make-up.'

She turned to me, and I saw the full technicolour horror of what she'd done in close-up. Her tangerine face was quite incongruous next to the paleness of her neck and hairline. It was then that I spied a bottle labelled Sudden Tan – a night-tan solution by Coppertone.

Only when I suggested that she follow me to the bathroom mirror with its harsher lighting did Mildred realise the result of the previous night's bedtime beauty routine. Lashings of Sudden Tan had left her with, as the bottle stated, a 'bronze tan that will last for days'.

Had Larry not seen me enter our building earlier, he'd have surely called the police; such was the volume of Mildred's shrieks.

Several basins of hot soapy water and a face scrub borrowed from Joanna's toilet bag later, she'd reduced the guaranteed 'all-over realistic glow' to a still pretty vibrant bronze. I forbade her from using household surface cleaner, but after forty minutes in the bathroom I was left so worn down that I let her have a go with the scrubbing brush designed for cleaning saucepans.

In the depths of her original 1930s monogrammed Max Factor make-up box, Mildred eventually found a solution: a bottle of hair whitening powder. She applied a cloud of the stuff. When the dust settled, the effect had indeed lessened the orange but left her with an Elizabethan look.

The doorbell rang.

I went to let in Howard and warn of the catastrophe that had occurred. I made it clear that he should say nothing.

***

Mildred was still asleep the next morning when Howard phoned. He said she'd enjoyed herself immensely at the House of Hardy Amies on Savile Row the previous night, telling anyone who would listen of her war years installed at the Savoy with Sir Hardy as her luncheon companion. I asked Howard about the reaction to her face. He said that of course people had commented to him. Good friends Ben and Angie Glazier joked privately that perhaps Mildred had mistaken Max Factor for McDougalls Flour.

William Tallon, otherwise known as 'Backstairs Billy', the stalwart and extrovert member of the late Queen Mother's staff at Clarence House, apparently had actually mentioned the whitened face to Mildred, who had pretended not to know what he meant.

Howard said that William, in a very smart black suit and impeccable foundation and eye-liner, had made Mildred laugh, and had asked why she had decided to rock up dressed as an 'old queen'; to which Mildred had asked, 'What old queen?'

William's riposte: 'Well, you've not come as 'this old queen', that's for sure.'

Home from work, I found Mildred in the recliner. She was wearing a cooling face mask. She asked that I sit with her while she excitedly recounted the events of the last night. I asked what reaction the face received. Knowing her as well as I did, I could tell when she lied. She said nobody noticed. She dismissed any thought of dinner, as that night she was out again: this time, a party at the private members' club, The Groucho. What was more, Howard had got me an invite too. Mildred was adamant that she wouldn't go unless I accompanied them both. She clapped with glee when I told her I would. Before I knew it she was heading back to the make-up room.

Excited at the prospect of a night out, and certain Joanna wouldn't mind as she had school tomorrow, I had a quick shower and planned which shirt to wear and whether I should wear a tie, and if so, which one.

It was obvious once we were at the party that Mildred hadn't given a thought to one of our group being left at the flat. She sandwiched herself between Howard and myself and she referred to us with wide beaming smiles as 'my matched pair'. Joanna was surplus to demand.

The next day, despite coming home late that night, Mildred was up early. She barged into our bedroom, put her hand on her hip, and said in a dismissive tone, 'Joanna. It's too bad Howard couldn't get you into the party last night.' Mildred's newfound social success was encouraging her snobbish side, a sense of self-importance that made her talk down to people. In those few days, it was directed at Joanna.

Joanna brought her knees up to her chest in our bed and smiled pensively. 'A night in the flat alone, with the telly and a glass of wine – honestly Mildred, I wasn't bothered.' And she hadn't been. Joanna was starting to find Mildred and her endless Hollywood stories suffocating.

Seven

Christmas

*A*s Christmas of 2003 approached, Mildred applauded Joanna's notion of perhaps buying a Christmas
tree for the flat. I guessed she'd bring it up and, just
as I predicted, in one of the two-dozen voice messages she left on my mobile while I was at work one day,
Mildred mentioned the old Christmas lights slung over
the washing line on the kitchen balcony. Her rambled
recording let me know that she'd spent 'forever' untan-
gling them, naïve to the fact they were quite possibly
lethal – the fittings and bulbs were completely rusted.
Not wishing to be electrocuted, I told Mildred that
evening that, while she'd been gossiping on the phone
to Zsa Zsa Gabor in Beverly Hills, I'd tested the lights
and they had failed. Thankfully Mildred didn't ask me
for a demonstration. She put the catastrophe of the
lights down to her landlord, the Duke of Westminster,
adamant that his penny-pinching was denying her the
correct wattage.

'I'm telling you, Suzie,' alleged Mildred, on the phone
to her friend Suzanne Kaaren, 'the Duke is denying me
the same electric current as my neighbours. Why else
would my perfectly good Christmas lights not work?

Geoffrey and I used them for years. They cost a fortune from Derry & Tom's on Kensington High Street.'

Derry & Tom's had ceased trading in 1971.

With a bee in her bonnet over her lights, Mildred began increasingly to point the finger at the Duke and believed him to be the reason she'd started to have trouble hearing the television. She resolutely poo-pooed my suggestion that she might need new hearing aids.

After the success of Thanksgiving, Joanna and I decided we would first ask my parents if they'd welcome the idea of Mildred coming to visit for Christmas, and then ask Joanna's parents about New Year.

To get into the Christmas spirit still further, Joanna suggested we attend a carol concert at St. Mary's. Mildred was ecstatic.

Where there had once been joy, the previous few Christmas Days had been an annual low point for Mildred. She had always adored attending the annual carol concert and Midnight Mass at St Mary's with Geoffrey and Adeline, and sometimes Baby when she was home in London.

As a friend of Mildred's later told me, Mildred and Geoffrey flip-flopped across the Atlantic for years, each time with fewer and fewer possessions. Finally, the Steeles had settled permanently in London in the seventies, firstly in a smart, almost space-age flat close to Cheyne Walk, Chelsea (whence they skedaddled, still owing rent) and then for good in Kylestrome House. Mildred had ordered Geoffrey to call fellow Old Etonian, the Duke of Westminster, and talk to him cap-in-hand. The result had been the flat on a peppercorn rent.

Selena Walters told me that, prior to this, Mildred's

Christmases had been spent in her and Geoffrey's condo on Coldwater Canyon, California. The property had been sold for virtually nothing when Mildred – distraught at not having Baby close at hand – had insisted they just sell as fast as possible and go. This caused a further irreplaceable loss for their dwindling bank balance.

After the carol concert I got chatting with Cicely Paget-Bowman. She hadn't seen Mildred in some time. She asked when 'the daughter' was due to visit.

I knew Baby would be coming, but not until the summer. Cicely asked if Baby was still 'at the house'.

Baby had installed herself permanently at Adeline's contemporary ranch-style home atop a hill in Glendale, California. Adeline and her Texan husband Calvin Parker had purchased it during the late 1950s.

From what Cicely recalled, around nine years later, after Geoffrey's death, and while Mildred was at the house in Glendale on a month-long vacation, an accident had occurred resulting in Adeline breaking her hip. While she was in the hospital recuperating, it had been decided that she should leave her home and travel to London with Mildred to convalesce.

'Adeline was never happy in London,' said Cicely. 'She and Mildred fought like cat and dog – mostly over who was the sicker sister.'

Adeline had never returned to her home.

'Adeline stopped coming to church and then, unable to leave her, Mildred stopped coming too,' said Cicely, who also recalled that the former priest at St Mary's, Father John, would instead give them Holy Communion at the flat.

'Father John told me he'd get pounced on before he'd even stepped over the threshold,' said Cicely. 'I can't imagine quite what it must have been like for a Father – both the Shay sisters anxious for his attention, eager to share even the most intimate of health issues.'

Adeline had ended her days occupying Mildred's cramped second bedroom. As sickness ravaged her and dementia set in, Mildred, unable to cope with her increasingly aggressive sister, had reluctantly moved her into a nearby council-operated nursing home.

'The last time I saw Adeline, I was confronted with a barrage of abuse,' Mildred told me later that night, as three vodka martinis turned her melancholy. Hysterical, Mildred had fled the tiny nursing home room that Adeline shared with another elderly woman.

'My sister repeated the line Mother had exploded on me three decades before: "You were nothing but a Hollywood whore."' Mildred wept at the anguish of recounting what Adeline said next. 'My perfectly wonderful sister hit me, and she screamed, "And you only got work through your cunt." I never forgot it.'

It had been the last time she saw her sister.

Mildred told me that since Adeline's death in 1998 she'd only managed two trips to California. She couldn't afford the airfare.

* * *

The run-up to Christmas Eve had gone smoothly. No doctor, no pestering the priest, no upset with Baby, no attacks by an 'over-sexed' Rosebud. It seemed that, having enjoyed the carol concert and a catch-up with old church friends, now the prospect of sharing two family Christmases was too much of a thrill for Mildred to let illness to spoil the fun. Ever since we had finished work for the holidays two days before, Mildred had been behaving like a five-year-old. She got into the Christmas spirit, withdrawing money from the account she shared with Baby (comprising of little else but Mildred's UK state pension), and asked Joanna to accompany her on a shopping spree to the Sainsbury's at Victoria Station, where she bought gifts. Her elation quickly turned sour, however; she was worried about her depleted savings, and thinking that Baby might need it more, she asked Howard to return all the gifts to the store, apart from the ones for him, Joanna, her mum, my mother, Rosebud, and me.

Mildred couldn't get on with sticky tape – not since she'd foolishly listened to her actress friend from the thirties, Shirley Chambers, who during their weekly transatlantic gossip revealed she'd been using Ginger Rogers' bargain age-defying technique of using sticky tape to 'hold the years back'.

Inspired, Mildred had decided to try the technique for herself. She called me at ten in the morning on my mobile – the third call of the day. I let it go to answerphone.

'Oh, Orstin, it's Cissie. Call me, it's urgent!'

I asked my boss if I could leave work early – again.

Mildred likened my slowly peeling the sticky tape from her face and hair to torture. 'Oh, Gawd, Orstin, I'm not into pain, darling,' she said, her voice pleading as I tugged gingerly. 'I tried S&M once and honestly, darling, the dressing up I loved, but the rest of it I couldn't get into.'

So with sticky tape a no-no and gift paper deemed too expensive, Mildred opted instead to wrap the presents in moth-eaten silk scarves and handkerchiefs, tied together with string or little bits of coloured ribbon, or even lace from old underwear she'd hidden away 'just in case.' The sentiment was there.

Sitting in the recliner, Mildred wrote gift tags on recycled Christmas cards from the previous year. She added a lipstick kiss and Baby's name to her own to wish us all 'A Merry and Peaceful Christmas and New Year'.

Mildred woke very early in anticipation of a phone call from Lady Janet, who'd been given detailed instructions on how to care for Rosebud while we were away – despite the fact she had looked after the cat, as well as her own menagerie of pets, for the best part of fifteen years. I heard them on the phone. Mildred was so overbearing that I felt surprised Lady Janet was still on the line.

Joanna and I had packed the night before Christmas Eve; Mildred had been packing in preparation for a week. It appeared Mildred didn't travel light. After several trips to and from the car, Joanna and I managed to squeeze in Mildred's luggage, comprising of two suitcases, Max Factor make-up box, leatherette jewel case, a hat box from Peter Jones and another from Marshall and Snellgrove, riding boots (to take walks in through the forest), golf clubs (she hadn't played golf since the fifties), two mink coats and one chinchilla.

Once Mildred had checked and re-checked that the front door and windows were locked, and rung Lady

Janet twice, and decided on a costume change from a dull brown Hardy Amies two-piece to a scarlet jacket and black t-shirt with a glittery silver star on the front, we were ready to go. Well, once Howard arrived. He rang my mobile and said he was around the corner. I checked my watch.

With Joanna eager to get on the road, we decided to wait for Howard in the carpark.

We were hardly out from the main doors when Mildred spotted Lord and Lady Davidson. She informed them in the grandest of voices that we were heading for the coast and then to the country. The Davidsons were terribly pleased for her, though couldn't spare another ten minutes as they were expecting a phone call.

Mildred spied her next victim, giving the same spiel to the ex-Speaker of the House of Commons and new arrival to the Cundy Street Flats, Baroness Boothroyd. Betty rather forcefully (in the same manner I'd seen her use on the television) said she had to go. I'd almost got Mildred in the car when she spied Lord Tom King.

It was obvious that they'd never met. Regardless, he stood patiently with his newspaper under his arm as Mildred informed him of her plans for the holidays. 'Do visit me, won't you?' she said, while at the same time calling for Joanna. 'Your father, dear, what's his name again?' asked Mildred.

'Ken Gabb,' said Joanna politely, but all the while looking at her wristwatch. Then, correcting herself, she called to Mildred, 'It's actually Kenneth, my dad is Kenneth Gabb.'

Mildred looked away from Joanna to Tom King. 'Oh,

well, Tom, darling – may I call you Tom?' she asked – he nodded. 'Well, my good man, if you're in the Cotswolds do look me up. As my little friend Joanna here says, I'll be residing over Old Year's Night with the Gabbs of Cinderford,' she said, her voice haughty. 'Daddy's a big noise, owns a factory.'

While Tom King looked bemused and Joanna rolled her eyes, I manoeuvred Mildred into the back of the car.

'Dad's gone up in the world,' said Joanna for my benefit as she opened the front passenger door.

Amazingly, Mildred heard her. 'Listen here, honey,' she said, her voice now broad New Yorker. 'I've learnt the hard way that ya gotta throw the shit around if ya wanna go places, see! Do you suppose these people would even give you the time of day, a school ma'am from the country? No, from the boondocks, for Christ's sake, that's where you're from, isn't it, dear?'

Mildred didn't wait for a complete answer, but Joanna shouted back, and loud. 'Nope!' shouted Mildred, even louder. 'They wouldn't, honey, so quit acting like you're some kinda feminist do-gooder and ham it up a bit once in a while!'

'Mildred, you can be a real bitch sometimes,' said Joanna, her voice cracking in anger. 'And leave my father out of this, he's a proud Labour man and not a factory owner – that was a lie!'

'Well, Labour men own factories too, and lots of them, and they drink champagne and they live in fucking big houses, so wise up!'

Joanna got out of the car and slammed the door. Mildred was still in full throttle.

'Mildred!' I yelled. 'What was all that for?'

'Lord King is an important man, for Christ's sake, and I don't want him thinking I'm a nobody! I'm Joseph A. Shay's daughter!' she yelled back. 'Joseph A. Shay, a man so bright he could have been President!'

'I get it,' I said as I opened the car door. 'But why launch at Joanna? She was correcting you – correcting your lie!' I spotted that Joanna had found Howard.

A quarter of an hour later I'd got Joanna back in the car. She and Mildred weren't speaking. No sooner had Joanna buckled up than Mildred asked to leave. She needed to make a pit-stop before we got going. Howard agreed to escort her to the flat to use the bathroom. This gave Joanna and I time to talk.

I agreed that I'd think about moving away from London. Joanna was about to start applying for permanent jobs in schools and had been looking at a post for an English teacher in Chepstow. Wales was a long way from the Cundy Street Flats.

I stroked Joanna's hair and promised that we would be moving on soon. I was lying, though; there was something about Mildred.

As usual, it was Joanna who said she'd back down first. She had decided she'd apologise to Mildred – her reason being, 'she's an old lady.' I was thankful. I couldn't bear the tension. Full of self-loathing, I told myself I was a coward. It was then I spied Howard emerging with Mildred. She was crying.

Mildred, in her black patent peep-toes, all but ran to Joanna. Mildred flung herself at her, and almost knocked me out with her handbag. Mildred was mortified that they'd argued. She was heartbroken at how mean she'd become after all the goodness and kindness Joanna had shown her.

'You're a beautiful woman, darling, and I'm an old crone,' she said, still embracing Joanna.

'But Mildred…'

Joanna couldn't get a word in.

'It's no good, darling, I'm telling the truth. I'm an old woman with a lost fortune who has nothing to give to my beautiful, clever, thoughtful Baby.'

'But you're kind and you're lovely…' said Joanna.

'Oh, keep going, dear,' said Mildred, 'I love the attention!' She was hurting, but she was masking it with humour. Mildred had done that her whole life.

'Oh, but Mildred…' repeated Joanna.

'I had everything and now I've nothing, and my poor Baby deserves the world. Oh, she's so ingenious! Her brain was bigger than other girls'. Her beauty stopped traffic! She was called 'America's Twiggy'…Baby could have been a rocket scientist.'

Mildred was still lamenting the plight as well as the genius of Baby as we finally got her seated and fastened in the back of the car. She asked that I fetch her jewel case from the boot, so she could have it on her lap for the journey. She also retained the chinchilla fur. I smiled to myself as I finally settled her in – she really looked like a movie star.

We didn't motor off just then – there was a further hitch. All the excitement had given Mildred indigestion. Finding a box of Rennies in her bag, Mildred popped two but felt she'd need more. The journey was delayed just once more as Howard leapt from the car to go back up to the flat and fetch more Rennies…

'Oh, and tissues,' Mildred said. She'd need more tissues, and a better mirror: her gold Asprey compact was too small. And a scarf, a woolly scarf, the one Joanna's grandmother knitted her, the exhilaration had given her a chill. She called after Howard. He was already at the main doors to her building. She flung open her door. 'Howard! Oh, Howard!'

I got out and, with a mental shopping list of Mildred's hopefully final requests, joined Howard. 'Boys!' she shouted, 'My matched pair! Make sure you give my Rosie a kiss too, dears. Oh, Gawd, Mama's never left her pussy alone for so long…' I looked back at Mildred. She was sniggering like a naughty schoolgirl. 'Oh, I'm awful,' she said.

Mildred talked all the way from Belgravia to Brighton. She spoke of Christmases past with her beloved Daddy and baby sister. The Christmas tree at the family mansion in Cedarhurst, New York, reached to the ceiling in the grand drawing room. The food, cooked and prepared by her favourite German-born 'Großmutter', filled the Shay home with a festive aroma. Our bellies rumbled as she recounted dishes of mashed sweet potato, roasted beetroot, green bean bake, snow-white turkey breast, and redcurrant sauce. 'Oh, those days were marvellous, Orstin,' she said from the back seat. 'Oma [the name she gave her Grandma] bottled and pickled all year in preparation for our Christmas Day feast. Oh, and the decorations! Well, listen here, Joanna; they were the talk of the neighbourhood. Mother was an exceptional decorator and Daddy, well, he was smart, he was clever, he could have been President!'

As Mildred told it, the Shays' residence in Cedarhurst was larger than the West Palm Beach estate with its bounty of bedrooms; there was a solarium, a swimming pool, and tennis courts. There were separate quarters for the maids, butler, and chauffeur. Mildred recalled how her grandmother had sacked the cook when she discovered her own cooking skills were far superior. Mildred usually got up at ten on Christmas morning. Her French maid helped get her dressed. Mildred would then rush to her grandmother's side and watch her wrestle with the turkey. The Shays ate their Christmas lunch at two o'clock. They used to eat at one until Mildred's mother discovered their West Palm Beach neighbours, E. F. Hutton and his cereal heiress wife, Marjorie Merriweather Post Hutton, ate at two, so moved proceedings back an hour.

Joanna was eyes-forward as Mildred jumped from one era to another: from Christmas in West Palm Beach and Christmas in Hollywood to Christmas as a young woman at the Shays' suite at the New York Plaza, and Christmas of late, alone with Rosebud. Unable to hear our replies, even when I stretched my head round from the front passenger seat and shouted back a response each time, Mildred continued to talk at us. As Mildred's back seat companion, Howard got the full brunt of it all. By the time we reached the A24 and Horsham, Joanna had switched on BBC Radio 2. Everyone except Mildred was exhausted. On the radio, Ken Bruce played *Maria* by Blondie.

The lyrics seemed strangely apt as I listened, thinking back to the time we first met and the stories. Oh, those stories…

The bombshell came when we were just five minutes away from my parents: Mildred wouldn't eat anything today. The pills she'd been taking to calm her dizzy spells had made her feel sick. There was silence, and then under her breath Joanna said, 'You've got to be kidding me.'

Preparations at my parents' house in Worthing were ongoing. My mother had been somewhat nervous about having Mildred as a house guest. She was frightened that Mildred might have a turn and demand an ambulance or a doctor. I had tried my best to put Mother at ease. I knew that once Mildred was over the threshold Mother's worries would be no more.

Howard called ahead on his mobile. I heard Father's voice, ever-enthusiastic about his children coming home. As we turned onto Hillside Avenue and into their driveway, he was there, ready to greet us, ready to open the passenger door and welcome Mildred. As soon as we had parked, he leant in and planted a kiss on Mildred's cheek.

'Hi, beautiful,' he shouted.

Father was visibly shocked by the amount of luggage Mildred had brought with her. 'Good gracious! Are you here for the month?' he said jokingly. Mildred didn't hear. She was overwhelmed with excitement.

Only two steps into the hall, Mildred was enthusing over Mother's décor, her choice of fabric and furnishings. 'Darling,' said Mildred, her arms aloft as Mother approached the front door from the living room, 'this house is beautiful. I love it.' Mother kissed Mildred on both cheeks. Mildred put her hand to her face. 'Thanks for giving me this, darling,' she said. 'I have been alone forever.' Mother's eyes were beginning to well up. It had been eight years since she had greeted her mother, my late grandmother Violet, in the same way on the doorstep – the fur coat, gloves, and hat were almost the same. But their demeanours couldn't have been more different. From my stories of her, Mildred had given Violet the nickname 'Lady Mutti'. She often told me they'd have gotten on famously. I rather felt Grandmother would have found Mildred most crude.

It wasn't long before Mother discovered this for herself.

Father and Howard brought in more bags. They piled them on the floor. Mother guided Mildred into the living room and proceeded to help her off with her mink. 'Oh, God, that's beautiful,' said Mildred in almost a scream as she noticed the Christmas tree twinkling. The light was reflecting off the French doors that lead out to the garden. 'I had perfectly good Christmas lights from Derry & Tom's,' said Mildred. 'Your son says they're no good,' she added, making a closer inspection of the tree. 'But it's not the lights, dear, it's my electricity. The Duke's syphoning it off elsewhere – he turns off my heating too. I'm freezing my arse off in London.'

With no mention of sickness, Mildred entertained my parents for three hours with the same stories Joanna, Howard, and I had heard in the car and many times over in the flat. Joanna excused herself. In the kitchen, she switched on the television and watched *The Two Ronnies*. Father kept Mildred's brandy glass topped up the entire time.

By the time we were ready to leave for the short drive to Midnight Mass, Mildred was pissed. Feeling exhausted, Mother, Father, and Joanna decided to stay put.

Mildred wiggled her way along the path leading to the church. The alcohol had left her animated. She greeted the vicar with open arms and planted a kiss on his cheek. 'Hello, vicar,' she said, and when she pulled away there was red lipstick on his cheek. 'I'm Mildred Shay from Hollywood.' She batted her false eyelashes at him and held court. It was the third time I'd heard her stories that day. Howard tried to move her towards a pew. Steadfast next to the vicar, she shook the hands of open-mouthed parishioners.

A stout woman whom I presumed to be the vicar's wife approached. Finally, with coaxing from me and at the insistence of the vicar's wife, Mildred left him alone.

The service was simple. Children filed up the aisle with candles at the end of the Mass. Mildred turned to me. 'God, it's a different business here in the country.' She looked about her. 'I mean, darling, some of these people are dressed for a trip to the supermarket.' Howard talked over her, trying to mask the volume of her criticism. As we prepared to leave, Mildred confronted the vicar. She congratulated him on the sermon.

'You know St. Mary's Bourne Street, of course?' said Mildred. The vicar nodded. 'Oh, you do? Well, it's my darling church close to my Belgravia residence. We get Kir Royales in the Presbytery when Mass finishes.'

The vicar's wife appeared, holding a jug. 'Oh, hello, dear,' Mildred said, looking her up and down. 'I was telling your husband here that at my church, St. Mary's, we have Kir Royales after Mass.' Mildred peered into the jug. 'What's that, dear? Orange squash?'

Discernibly annoyed at this interloper, the vicar's wife spoke up. 'Well, you won't be getting champagne here, and coffee's a pound, squash fifty pence.' Mildred ignored her.

Mildred remained at the vicar's side as the parishioners left. Once again she nodded and smiled at them as they filed past her. Intent on making herself known, Mildred took the liberty of shaking the hands of two young men and their wives. Mildred beamed as she lingered over the men. She was dismissive of the wives – until one asked for her autograph.

Back at my parents' house, Father opened a bottle of champagne. Mildred criticised the service, the vicar, and the congregation, leaving the vicar's wife to last. 'God, she was so fat, and no personality. She hardly said a word.' We went to bed at two o'clock.

The following morning, Christmas Day, I passed Mother on the landing. She was carrying a breakfast tray: hot tea, two boiled eggs, and soldiers. I was sitting at the breakfast table, tucking into grapefruit, when Mother reappeared. She was laughing. Mildred had been propped up in bed, Bible in one hand and Max Factor lipstick brush in the other, a turban on her head and her mink around her shoulders. 'I feel I've just paid a visit to Gloria Swanson,' said Mother. 'Goodness me, Mildred is awfully glamorous.'

Mildred appeared, carrying her breakfast tray. She'd changed into black trousers and a red blouse. She was wearing the gold Empress Eugenie necklace, diamond and platinum earrings, a brooch and a bracelet.

'Oh, Orstin, dear,' she said, plonking the tray before me, 'I thought you'd like an egg.' I broke into a hollow shell. This made her laugh. She told us how her brother Arnold used to play the same prank on her. He'd wait with bated breath for her reaction. 'It broke him up every time.'

Breakfast cleared away, Father suggested a walk along the prom. Mildred's reaction was what one might have imagined of a five-year-old. She clapped her hands before announcing she'd have to change. She kept everyone waiting for forty minutes. I went to her room, but it was hopeless. She wouldn't be rushed. Eventually satisfied with dark slacks, riding boots, and a polo-neck over which she was wearing what seemed like dozens of rows of pearls, we were ready. Mother looked at her watch as Mildred emerged. We would not have long for a walk.

Mildred stood at the far end of Worthing Pier, the wind lapping up sea-spray. She breathed deeply, allowing her lungs to be filled with cold sea air. She was determined to walk over the pebbles. Leaving the pier, with Mother on one side of her and me on the other, we managed to clamber to the water's edge. Mildred removed her right glove and put her hand in the sea, then patted the side of her cheek with her wet fingers, before she stepped back to avoid the waves with such haste that she almost toppled over and dragged Mother and me with her.

Back home, Father announced 'bar open'. Everyone gathered in the living room. All the colourfully-wrapped presents were under the Christmas tree. Mildred goggled at them. 'Can we open these now?' she asked Mother.

Father fetched the drinks; Mildred joined Mother and requested a sherry. She took a healthy gulp and then placed the crystal glass on a small yew table before tucking into the savoury snacks Mother had served in dishes dotted about the room. As Mildred drank, I became increasingly nervous – even more so than when I'd first taken Joanna home to meet them a few years before.

After a few more sherries Mildred's mouth did get carried away with itself. It had been over an hour since we had gathered to unwrap the Christmas gifts, and she hadn't stopped talking. Father played host, refilling glasses. Mother watched him.

'John, dear, that's enough of that,' she said eventually, motioning to the bottle of Harvey's Bristol Cream. 'Why don't you check on how the lunch is coming along in the kitchen?'

'Pamela,' smiled Mildred as she sipped her sherry, 'do you know your son has been living with me for an age now and hasn't shown me his penis once!' She took another gulp.

I intervened from the opposite sofa. 'Hey, come on, Mildred,' I said forcefully, 'Mother really is not interested…' She chose not to hear me.

'I mean, Pamela, darling,' Mildred continued, 'I haven't seen one for years.'

'Oh, dear,' said Mother, stumped.

Mildred giggled. 'When my beloved Geoffrey died at the age of seventy-two, my world ended,' said Mildred, knocking back the dregs in her glass. 'I told my doctor that Geoffrey and I had made love every morning, and you know what he suggested?'

Mother shook her head.

'Well, he said I should masturbate! Well, darling, I tried, but I'm just not my own type.' Father was in the hallway. I heard him laugh. Mother had visibly turned red, flustered. I was scarlet.

Having realised Mother had become jittery, Howard took control of the conversation, jumping to his feet to announce he'd be playing Santa by handing out gifts. He fetched a large soft package from under the tree and passed it to Mildred. The gift from Joanna and me. Mildred tore at the gold brocade paper and then at the tissue underneath before she revealed a baby-blue dressing gown with faux fur cuffs and collar.

'Oh, my God,' said Mildred. 'Who bought me this?'

'Austin and me,' beamed Joanna, who was visibly delighted by Mildred's gleeful expression. Mildred was beginning to cry.

'Oh, Lord, I said I wouldn't cry this year, but here I am, but my darlings, these are tears of joy.' Still overwhelmed, she looked about the room at all of us and wailed, 'I'm so happy.'

The remainder of the day ran smoothly. The only annoyance for Mother was that after lunch Mildred talked through the Queen's entire Christmas broadcast with a mouth full of mince pie. She told us about the time the Shays stayed at Balmoral. 'I gave it to the King on the second night of our stay,' she said. '"George," I said, "can't you find some more wood for the fires? I'm freezing my arse off!"'

Mother, a monarchist, waited until after the national anthem to respond. 'Good gracious, what did His Majesty say to that?' she asked Mildred.

'Oh, George was a doll and fetched me a dozen sweaters!' replied Mildred, and took another mince pie from the cake plate. 'I've still got a couple of them.' She turned to me.

'I've still got the King's sweaters, haven't I, Orstin?'

I wondered if these had been amongst the heap of moth-eaten clothes that Joanna and I had tossed out from the make-up room. The Argyle pullovers in the bag of men's clothes we had found had been chewed to bits.

Fortunately, Mildred noticed a trailer on the television for what an announcer described as an explosive episode of *Eastenders*: Kat and Alfie's wedding. Mildred lampooned Shane Richie's acting skills; she guffawed in horror at the actress playing Little Mo and labelled her talentless; however, she released her most venomous attack on the actress who was playing Nana Moon.

Mildred turned to Mother. 'What a crock of shit, Pamela! That's not acting!' she said, drawing Mother's attention to the television. 'I should call my agent and get a part on this show!'

As with Violet before her, Mother didn't watch soaps, nor much else besides nature programmes, the news, *Miss Marple*, *Antiques Roadshow*, and *Keeping Up Appearances*.

'My mother would often say television ruined the art

of conversation,' she said, as Mildred continued to criticise everyone who appeared.

Mother's decision to then turn the television off left Joanna, Father, and Howard heading for the hills. Joanna escaped to the kitchen, Father to his shed, and Howard to a neighbour, leaving just me, Mother, and Mildred.

Mildred dominated any discussion. When, during an afternoon tea of Earl Grey and Christmas cake, Mother happened to mention she'd visited Hampton Court with her chum Jackie recently, Mildred upstaged her with stories of partially living there with Geoffrey's nanny for a spell during World War II.

After we had heard half a dozen stories about the virtuoso that was Baby and the brilliance of her father's mind, as well as a further analysis of the cast of *Eastenders*, Mother mentioned for my benefit that she'd received a gift of Newberry Fruits from friends Tom and Win Gillon. She explained to Mildred that Tom had worked behind the scenes at the Old Vic Theatre. Certain they'd have known her, Mildred launched into a story of the time she'd headlined as Mrs Baker in *Come Blow Your Horn*. As she told it, Mildred out-shone the rest of the cast, with Neil Simon himself joining critics from Sutherland to Glasgow in singling out her telephone call monologue scene as the best thing they'd ever seen – ever!

By the time Mildred had finished a long oration celebrating her own performance as Janet Roscoe in Colin Dexter's *Inspector Morse*, Mother was halfway to the shed herself.

Drinks were served at six. The television had been on for an hour, and Mother turned up the volume louder and louder.

When Mildred was finally in bed, I helped Father unload the dishwasher. He poured me a nightcap. 'I tell you what,' he said, 'your mother and I are certain there's nothing Mildred hasn't done.'

On Boxing Day morning, we were waved off for the three-hour drive to Joanna's parents by Mother and Howard standing on the doorstep, while snow fell around us. Father had helped me load the luggage earlier while Mildred and Joanna were getting into their coats. He was on the driveway, clearing the windscreen of ice.

As I kissed Mother, she expressed the hope that Mildred would behave herself. 'I can't imagine Julie or her mother will appreciate talk of penises,' she said, still horrified. 'I would suggest to Julie you find a little television she can watch – she does an awful lot of talking!'

'See you again, gorgeous,' said Father as he helped Mildred into the car.

'Oh, Johnny,' said Mildred, 'I can see who your sons inherited their good looks from.'

He leant inside the car to kiss first Joanna, who was behind the wheel, and then Mildred.

'Johnny, do come to the flat and visit me,' she said, toying with the collar of her mink, her voice loud over the roar of the engine. 'It's in the right location, dear, and I've a real nice little pussy you can play with.' She bellowed at her own innuendo.

'She's a bloody laugh a minute!' said Father to me as I got into the car beside Joanna.

Mother's face told me she didn't agree; her smile was polite at best.

Lunch in Cinderford promised to be a re-run of Christmas Day, with all the trimmings. Thankfully Mildred slept most the journey, and only woke once we were coming into the city of Gloucester. Joanna suggested we visit the cathedral.

Inside, the three of us lit candles. I made a donation and lit a candle in memory of Violet. Joanna's dedication remained anonymous. Mildred dropped five pounds into a donation box and then proceeded to explain, in her loudest New Yorker voice, how she'd be lighting candles in memory of her darling husband Geoffrey, her brilliantly clever Daddy, her poor baby sister Adeline, and beautiful brother Arnold. The fifth candle was reserved for Baby; the eulogy so profound, so gushing, so long, that I wondered if we would make it to Cinderford before New Year's Eve.

'You heard my tribute to Baby,' said Mildred as we headed from the cathedral to the car.

'I did, Cissie.'

'Well, she's my world.' We walked in silence for a few paces. 'My priest in Beverly Hills called me once and said he was gonna give Baby ten dollars to get out of town! I asked why, and he said, "Because you're mothering her to death!"'

As with my mother, Mildred congratulated Julie on her flair for interior design and determined that Julie had perhaps the better eye for colour. 'Oh, darling woman,' said Mildred as she embraced Julie, 'you're so clever, dear – much more so than that Scottish female decorator on the television.' (I presumed she meant Carole Smiley.)

If the décor wasn't appetising enough, Julie had prepared a feast of roast pork with roasted vegetables, home-made apple sauce, and red currant jelly. Mildred ate every morsel, including a creamy trifle. Over coffee and mints, Mildred entertained Julie, Kenneth, and Joanna's brother Jonny with tales of Hollywood, climaxing with her 'affair' with Victor Mature. Joanna decided to video her – while the camera was rolling, nobody else got a word in.

The extended family turned out in force during the late afternoon: Joanna's sister Rachael, her statuesque husband Jason, and their children Minnie and Benjamin arrived around four. Less interested in Rachael, Mildred flirted with Jason outrageously and left him in hysterics as she told him about her conquests in Hollywood.

Mildred was particularly intrigued by a photograph in the dining room of Kenneth's father in his World War I uniform. Later, the family – now joined by Joanna's grandparents, Betty and Roy – sat in the living room, while Mildred remained at the dining table with Kenneth and me. We drank whiskey as he shared what he knew of his father. In turn, she told us about her dearest Geoffrey's military career and her experiences staying at the Savoy in London. One of the most memorable anecdotes was how she first met American journalist and commentator Bob Considine, best known as the co-author of *Thirty Seconds Over Tokyo* and *The Babe Ruth Story*.

'It was 1944. I was in the Savoy restaurant,' she said. 'I spotted Bob nibbling morosely on a hunk of dry English brown bread, so I offered him a hunk of golden balm' – butter – 'and we got on famously ever after.'

As the day turned to night, Minnie and Benjamin played with 'Great Aunty Mildred'. Later, and with no persuasion necessary, Benjamin put on his own special performance for us when we settled down in the living room, with Jack the dog at Mildred's feet in front of a roaring fire.

Mildred headed upstairs to bed around ten – but before that, she pulled Julie aside in the hall. Betty had complained throughout the evening of having a headache. Mildred had become convinced Betty undoubtedly had a brain tumour. She urged Julie to call a doctor, but not before she asked if she could borrow the phone so she could call Baby in California.

'I'm telling you, Julie, dear, I saw it during the War when I travelled these parts with the USO – country folk who'd just pop an extra lump of coal on the fire or pull on an extra sweater, even though they'd got double pneumonia or worse, because they didn't have the wits about them to call a doctor.'

Julie battled to convince Mildred that her mother simply had a headache. 'Oh, Julie, my dear,' Mildred pleaded from over the banister, 'I'm certain without a proper qualified specialist your mother could die!'

Angered, Julie stormed from the hall into the kitchen, where she found Kenneth, Jonny, and me. We had heard every bit of the confrontation. Julie left it to Kenneth to fetch Mildred the phone. 'Oh, Oz,' Julie said to me furiously, 'I'm not going to let her worry our mum like that! Oh, I tell you what, I very nearly got my hair off with her then! Oh, she's right irked me, she has, mind.'

Kenneth took the phone to Mildred, who was spread-eagled on top of the bed in the smallest of the guest bedrooms. Phone in hand, she asked if Kenneth could fetch her some water. She felt sure she had a hangover brewing and needed to take aspirin. She shook four from a bottle beside her. Kenneth filled a glass and left her to it.

The following morning, Mildred announced she'd like to join Joanna, Jonny, Kenneth, Jack the dog, and me for a stroll through the forest. She felt she needed to get her legs moving more and a walk in the country would be the perfect solution. We waited for Mildred in the hall. She had been in her bedroom preparing herself for the walk for twenty minutes. When she did appear, I could only describe the look as something akin to one of the Ewoks in *Star Wars*. She was in full make-up, wearing a roll-neck, over which she had an Argyle jumper, a woolly scarf, and her mink. She was also carrying the chinchilla. She was sporting a headscarf tied under her chin and on top of that a woolly hat with a fur pom-pom.

'Oh, for goodness' sake,' I said loudly, 'Mildred's morphed into early caveman colliding with Benny from *Crossroads*.'

Joanna managed to tease the chinchilla from her and the woolly hat. Kenneth wondered what the locals would make of her. Jack just stared. I detected a faint snarl. 'They'll run away,' I joked. 'She's the Abominable Snowman!'

Mildred sneered. 'Orstin, need I tell you I entertained the troops in open-air theatres in these parts? Really, darling, the air is different here, I'm certain of it. When I returned to London I was covered in bites.'

'Bed bugs, perhaps, Mildred?' suggested Kenneth.

'Oh, you think so?' said Mildred quizzically. 'Well, I was bed-hopping amongst the soldiers!' She roared with laughter. 'Just to keep 'em warm,' she smiled. 'Oh, you must think I'm awful.'

'I don't think I've ever met anyone like you,' replied Kenneth, taking Jack by the lead.

Our walking party certainly met with some odd looks. Ramblers did double-takes just to be sure Mildred was real. Every time a new person – especially of the male variety – approached, Mildred greeted them with an astounding 'Good day' or 'Hello, my fine man, nice weather we're having.'

We managed three miles of the Beechenhurst Trail. Despite our insisting we stop and turn tail back towards the car, Mildred was adamant we keep walking. We all collapsed in the sunroom when we got back to the house. Julie had been quite worried. 'I nearly called Air and Rescue, mind,' she said jokingly. Mildred took her seriously.

'Oh, darling, imagine it! My being rescued off a mountain. Why, I'd be the talk of the Cundy Street flats, and what would Baby say?'

Rather than alleviating her aches and pains with exercise, by the late afternoon Mildred had taken to her bed. The family had returned for afternoon tea and were gathered in the living room. It was Rachael who heard

Mildred's cries first. I rushed up the stairs two at a time, with Jason directly behind me. Mildred was rubbing her calf muscle and claimed she'd been sneezing. She needed a doctor. I laughed at first – there was no way a doctor would come out for such a simple prognosis. But Mildred was not amused. She was certain it would soon develop into something more serious unless she saw a doctor 'immediately'. I'd rarely seen her quite so angry. Jason did his best to calm her down, even offering a massage, but, waving her fists in our faces, she became more agitated. An increase in her blood pressure would finish her off before muscle cramp or any common cold. On top of this, she was rubbing her chest. Mildred was certain that she was having a heart attack. I left the room and closed the door on her, worried that I'd say something I'd regret. Joanna was on the landing with Kenneth, Julie, and Rachael.

'Oh, what's happening, Oz?' said Julie, as she took hold of my hand. She turned to Kenneth: 'Oh, Ken, what should we do?'

Julie jumped and Rachael screamed when the door suddenly flew open.

'Oh, please, get me a doctor!' cried Mildred, tugging at her hair in frustration. Julie scurried for the phone in their bedroom. She got on the line to the local hospital, the Dilke. 'She's an American, mind,' said Julie to a voice on the other end of the line.

'Tell them I'm a movie star from Hollywood, for Christ's sake,' shouted Mildred. 'That'll bring out the big guns!'

There was nobody available for a home visit; in truth,

in her panic, Julie forgot to mention the palpitations, so Mildred was deemed fit enough for Joanna and I to take her to the Dilke. But she would not leave until her make-up had been fixed.

After thirty anxious minutes, Mildred descended the staircase and then, without a word, swept past the family amassed in the hall. She was wearing her pink track-suit, black patent court shoes, and mink. Despite the fact that it was dark, she was wearing sunglasses and a candy-pink headscarf tied under her chin.

'Bloody hell, Oz,' said Jason, stunned. 'She looks like Elizabeth Taylor, mind!'

Mildred stopped at the front door to put on leather gloves. I noticed she'd reapplied her nail varnish. She was wearing more jewellery than she had been earlier, including a vast diamond ring.

She retrieved a bottle of Giorgio Beverly Hills from her pocketbook, squirted four times, flung it back in her bag and, with a snap of the clasp, grabbed my arm, leaving the family on the doorstep in a perfumed mist.

Joanna, Mildred and I were the only people in the waiting room. After ten minutes, and three short coughs, Mildred became irate. She spied a nurse. To save the nurse from her wrath, I jumped to my feet. Mildred was called moments later and whisked off to a side room. Joanna decided to listen in and disappeared around the corner to find her. But after just a few minutes, Joanna was back. From the other side of the door, she had heard Mildred talking the doctor through her wallet of photographs.

'She's telling the doctor about being attacked by Errol

Flynn and the size of Frank Sinatra's todger!' said Joanna, exasperated.

Mildred appeared in the waiting room with her fur around her shoulder, swinging her glasses in her hand. 'I have gas,' she said, chewing on indigestion tablets. 'Isn't that awful!'

I waited with Mildred in the reception as Joanna fetched the car. 'Let me tell you something,' said Mildred as I buckled her up and she pulled another Rennie from its foil wrapping. 'My mother couldn't eat cream after pork either.'

'You ate the roast pork and trifle over forty-eight hours ago!' I argued.

'Oh, you've caught me out,' she said, ashamed. 'I was hungry so last night I had a midnight snack.'

'Naughty Mildred!' said Joanna, laughing at her admission. 'Mum blamed Jonny for finishing off the pudding and leaving the empty bowl in the fridge!'

Mildred asked that I bid goodnight to Kenneth, Julie, and the family on her behalf. She was sure the visit to the Dilke in the cold night air had worsened her chill. 'That doctor was just a kid, darling. He was rather cold with me too. I wonder if he is fully trained.'

The next morning, Mildred was up and about, if a little sheepish. She found me in the small sunroom off the kitchen. Julie, Kenneth, and the others had left a short while ago for a walk along the Ruffet. Mildred took a seat next to me. She asked that I listen, and not interrupt. She reminded me that Baby was all she had and vice versa. That Baby couldn't take the stress of having a sick Mama, what with her worries about Gordon, the dogs, the birds, the cats, and Sun, her horse. Mildred took my hand in hers. 'For Baby's sake, both emotionally and financially,' she told me quite seriously, 'Orstin, I've gotta live forever.'

My heart jumped. Forever is a long time.

Eight

Diet and Exercise

*A*s spring approached, Mildred made an announce-
ment: we would have to move out.

It was Sunday night and, knowing that at any minute
Mildred would make her phone call to Baby, as she always did at that time, Joanna and I decided to go for a
drink and bite to eat at the Duke of Boots. Joanna had
left Mildred a light snack: a Caesar salad she'd prepared
earlier. When reminded that it was in the fridge, Mildred said she'd not touch it. She was on a diet.

Mildred had informed us earlier that she'd watched
Atkins Diet devotee Geri Halliwell on *This Morning*
and thought that 'the ginger one from the pop act'
looked gorgeous. I was amazed. Mildred hardly ever
had anything good to say about her own sex, let alone
celebrities like the Spice Girls. Mildred used to loathe
Posh Spice in particular – until she happened to meet
Victoria Beckham with Howard at one of his co-or-
dinated events. Afterwards, Mildred was positively
glowing with admiration but left the loudest applause
for her husband, David. Ever flummoxed by how a
footballer could have amassed such a fortune, each
time she saw his face in her *Daily Express* newspaper
she'd screech, 'Oh, honestly! What does he do besides

kicking a ball around? Big deal!' No matter, she was still sweet on him.

Aside from admiring Gerri Halliwell, Mildred had also been looking through Joanna's copy of *Marie Claire* magazine and had decided, aged ninety-two, to get her bikini body back. I teased her as she ate her breakfast of muesli and yoghurt that her body predated the invention of the bikini – that perhaps a one-piece bathing suit, Mack Sennett-style, would be more her vintage. She stuck out her tongue at me before looking down the top of her pyjamas at her breasts. 'Come back, boys,' she sighed.

In the Duke of Boots, I got the drinks while Joanna popped to the loo. The bathroom in the flat had been otherwise occupied. After countless spats with Joanna over Rosebud continuing to shit about the flat, Mildred had started trying to toilet train the cat. If Mildred wasn't trailing Rosebud around with her food bowl, then she would be behind her with some form of receptacle, asking if she needed a pee-pee. We had soon put a stop to her using the cut-glass fruit bowl. Despite protests that we needed to use the toilet before leaving the flat, Mildred had asked that we not disturb Rosebud. Mildred had shut her in the bathroom with the toilet seat up, insisting Rosebud needed space and privacy if she were to perform.

At the pub, Joanna asked for a gin and slimline tonic. I ordered a pint of Guinness for myself. Within minutes, I got talking to an old boy wearing a ginger demi-wave toupée. I'd seen him propping up the bar pretty much every time Joanna and I had been in.

Leonard, as it turned out, had been a hairdresser

aboard the HMS *Queen Mary*. He accepted a second pint of Guinness from me. As it happened, he'd left his wallet in his other ('Savile Row', he mentioned) coat. We got talking some more.

Leonard had known Mildred's Geoffrey. He remembered him as a devilishly handsome man with a pencil-thin moustache, not unlike David Niven. Leonard recalled Geoffrey's demeanour being akin to that of Leslie Phillips: suave, charming, with an exaggerated upper-class accent and an eye for the ladies. Leonard wasn't the first to mention Geoffrey's friendships with Lady Lucan and local celebrity Sarah Churchill, nor that he had been all too often 'a bit short'.

After quizzing me further on Geoffrey, Leonard launched into a tale of Lady Lucan running into the pub – 'just where you're standing now, sir,' he said. He likened her dishevelled appearance to something ghoulish from a Hammer horror film – 'covered in blood, she was, screaming, crying for help! There'd been a murder and her husband Lord Lucan, he'd done it!' Leonard's raised voice attracted the attention of Gareth, the barman, a smiley young chap whom Joanna and I had got to know quite well.

After accepting just another half of Guinness from 'my kind lady' Joanna, Leonard continued his story. Gareth was now listening in too. Leonard was positive Geoffrey Steele had been in the pub that night – and added a perhaps rather implausible detail to his account: that Geoffrey had offered Lady Lucan shelter at his home. I could not imagine Geoffrey believing Mildred would be able to cope in such a crisis.

Gareth interrupted Leonard, who was still in full flow. While Lady Lucan had indeed run into a pub, it hadn't been this one, but the Plumbers Arms on Lower Belgrave Street. His story tainted, Leonard cursed Gareth's rudeness. He was unhappy that the youngster should have 'earwigged in on a gentleman's private conversations'.

We finished our drinks at a table by the door. Leonard stayed up at the bar, joined by the former *Crossroads* actress Sue Lloyd, the pair of them not waiting for the other to finish as they waged tirades on the stars they'd known.

Leonard: 'Omar Sharif was a gambler but a good tipper. Sean Connery – he was a meanie with his money.'

Sue: 'Noele Gordon was a bitch, it was Nolly this and Nolly that...'

Back at the flat, we had hardly had time to remove our coats when Mildred began bellowing at us from the recliner. Baby had called her that evening. Mildred waxed lyrical about the splendour of her perfectly beautiful Baby and how thoughtful she was to her Mama. 'Darlings,' she announced, 'Mama's pride and joy, my precious Baby-girl, is coming to London!'

Perhaps it wasn't a complete surprise. The one major ground rule on our moving in had been that one day, one 'beautiful, heaven-sent' day, Baby would return to Mama and we would have to find alternative accommodation.

Plans were set in motion. Joanna could return home in two months' time to her parents, as it'd be the school summer holidays anyway. I could join her there on weekends. For the first two weeks, I'd arranged to stay with Kirsty on the sofa bed at her flat in Streatham during the week. Then, for the third and final week of Baby's vacation, I'd stay with Corinne in Walton-on-Thames, Surrey.

Mildred spent the weeks leading up to the arrival of Baby on an even more regimented diet. She asked to intervene in the menu for the week ahead. She'd not be eating carbohydrates, nor desserts, sweets, or candy. And only vodka, no wine.

Mildred located a stack of A6 gold-edged blank menu cards in one of the Louis Vuitton trunks. She asked Joanna to sit in the library chair so they could discuss meals for the week ahead. She decided on plenty of red meat, just as Dr David Gurewitsch, personal physician to Eleanor Roosevelt, had prescribed to Mildred's mother during the 1930s. She would suffer rice, even though she didn't really like it. And fish, but only if hadn't been 'messed about with' – she preferred it plain with a squeeze of lemon. Nothing fancy; she couldn't abide seeds and nuts.

I was in the kitchen when Joanna came in with Mildred's scribbled suggestions.

'And to think before we arrived she lived on vodka martinis and Ritz crackers,' sighed Joanna as she tossed the five menu cards on the counter.

As the time for Baby's arrival edged closer, Mildred was up in the mornings way before Joanna and me. Fully clothed in exercise gear (of sorts), she climbed aboard the old exercise bike she'd asked me to retrieve from the kitchen balcony.

But after a few days, she was unable to cope with what she described as her 'silent journey to no-place,' so Joanna suggested she listen to some music. Joanna found a selection of CDs at the local library which Mildred could listen to while cycling. Mildred soon discovered she most liked riding to the 1977 Tom Jones album *What a Night* and *The Best of Barry Manilow* – her favourites were *Tryin' To Get The Feeling Again* and *Looks Like We Made It*.

Only she didn't make it. After a few days, the bike was back on the balcony. The next morning, sporting a new look – a black shiny leotard – she began lumbering about the living room to a Jane Fonda workout video. When Jane's boundless energy proved too strenuous, she telephoned and asked Zsa Zsa Gabor to send her a copy of her own keep-fit video.

The video arrived in the post. Calum the postman rang the doorbell but didn't wait for her to answer – much to her annoyance since Calum was her favourite postman eye-candy. Mildred took the white jiffy envelope with Zsa Zsa's Bel-Air address on the top left-hand corner to the living room. She called me to show off the enclosed note from 'The Desk of Zsa Zsa Gabor'. It was a scribbled message: 'To Mildred, remember, it's easy, darlink!'

'What the hell is she talking about?' queried Mildred, before realising it was the title of the video.

Mildred asked that I stick the tape into her VHS recorder. Shot in soft focus, the tape opened with Zsa Zsa in a plunging pink evening gown, drenched in diamonds. While Joanna and I busied ourselves about the flat, Mildred was glued to the TV screen. She paused it part-way through, rose, and slipped off to her bedroom. In copycat mode, she emerged sporting a sort of emerald green and gold kaftan over a leopard-print leotard, which she informed us Baby had bought for her. The item sagged rather than clung. It had undoubtedly been purchased a very long time ago.

Joanna and I watched from behind the living room door in hysterics as Mildred started to bend and stretch, bump and grind, in just the way Zsa Zsa showed her. Zsa Zsa promised that following her lead three times a week would guarantee that you stayed young, beautiful, and sexy forever, not to mention helping you 'drive your man crazy'.

Mildred didn't make it past two of Zsa Zsa's exercise routines. She was sure Zsa Zsa had engaged a body-double and thought that without the aid of Mike and François, Zsa Zsa's muscle-bound hunks, the routine was quite miserable.

Seeing Mildred so desperate to regain her figure in order to impress Baby, Joanna came to the rescue with the Angela Lansbury *Positive Moves* workout video, picked up at the East Ham branch of the Sue Ryder charity shop close to her school. Promising to aid fluidity, grace, and movement, Angela Lansbury was a sure-fire hit.

Mildred called Baby nightly to make sure she was still coming. Determined to stay well, Mildred was now alarmed by any minor twinge.

* * *

Despite leaving me voice messages during the day explaining what had caught her attention on *The Lorraine Kelly Show* that morning, she was waiting by the front door when I got home. She was worried.

Lorraine had been speaking to a woman who'd suffered a reaction to the flu vaccine. I consoled her that the show must be short of content if they were running a feature on flu vaccines in the height of the summer. Mildred questioned whether I'd ever heard of summer colds. I pretended I hadn't.

Unable to bear any further 'Baby' talk, Joanna had decided to get away and visit her friend Michelle in Wales for the weekend. I was left home alone with Mildred and Rosebud. Mildred liked it that way.

She suggested we go to St. Mary's on Sunday. She'd like to tell 'everybody' that Baby was coming to see 'Mama'.

* * *

Before Joanna and I had arrived, St. Mary's had offered Mildred a lifeline. However, being unsteady on her feet, she couldn't always get there, much to the sorrow of one particular admirer: the former Tory MP, the Earl of Lauderdale.

'She can always be counted upon to put on a bloody good show,' said ninety-five-year-old Lord Lauderdale, delighted I'd 'arrived on the scene', as he put it, and was occasionally able to bring Mildred to church.

In the presbytery after the service he and I chatted – the subject was, of course, Mildred. He watched adoringly as she mingled with fellow parishioners – the only topic of conversation being Baby.

While still staring at Mildred, Lord Lauderdale recounted for me one rather showy performance during Holy Communion.

'The woman's skirt flew off, just like in that pop act, Bucks-something or other.' He scoffed at my notion that Mildred perhaps might have been embarrassed that her elastic had snapped, causing her skirt to fall down in the presence of God. 'Not one bit, my good man! She wasn't fussed – a game old bird, she simply stepped out of it and carried on regardless – a bloody marvellous woman!'

Unable to contain himself any longer, Lord Lauderdale asked that I help him to his feet and then, refusing any further assistance, shuffled over to greet Mildred with a bow and a kiss to her hand.

'How are you, my Lord?' she asked.

'All the better for seeing you, my dear,' he said with a grin.

Back at the flat, Mildred told me she'd been spurning Lord Lauderdale's advances for years. 'I don't want old flesh crawling all over me.'

* * *

That night, Mildred went through old photographs that she thought might be of interest to Baby. While I was chopping vegetables, Mildred shoved photos of her beloved Geoffrey under my nose. She found one of the last photos she had of him.

Leaning against the sink with tears in her eyes, Mildred recounted how Geoffrey had died of multiple organ failure during their visit to see Baby and Adeline at Adeline's house in 1987. Distraught and needing her own time and space to mourn, Baby took herself off to California's horse-riding country.

Before bed, Mildred insisted I joined her in praying for Baby's safe passage, and that she and Baby enjoyed their reunion in every conceivable way. I opened my eyes half-way through. Mildred's were closed as she prayed that Baby's high IQ and genius brain would help her land a good job and overcome her addiction to Gordon. She prayed for all Baby's animals and all Baby's friends. She became so worked up that she asked me to leave the room. I did. Behind me, Mildred sank into her pillow and sobbed her heart out.

Baby, Mildred told me the next day, had had a privileged childhood and, like Judy Garland's daughter Liza Minnelli, was 'raised amongst stars'. Baby's friends were all the children of celebrities (a few of them were Mildred's former beaus). Mildred told me how Baby had bounced as an infant on Boris Karloff's knee, and was often with her and Geoffrey at Cary Grant's house parties. She had played cowboys and Indians with John Carradine's sons, Keith and David, or kiss chase with Stacy Keech Jr. after Sunday School at St. Michael's and All Angels, Glendale, where Stacy Sr. and Geoffrey were churchwardens. Baby had often been invited to play with Roy Jnr and his other siblings in the garden of Roy Rogers' Beverly Hills mansion. Mildred admitted with a snigger that, meanwhile, she had been 'ridin' around with Roy!'

Mildred found me again an hour later when I was sitting on my bed reading. She sat on the edge of my bed and told me again of Baby's brilliance. Apparently, Baby's teachers at Grant High and Hollywood Professional School had said she could pursue a career as a physicist, a rocket scientist, or at the very least a professor, but how, with striking looks at sixteen – tall, blonde and beautiful – she was destined for life as a model. She had mixed with every conceivable talent in swingin' Sixties London, downing brandy and ginger with Ringo Starr and Keith Moon, occasionally playing with their drumsticks. Escaping from 'Mama', she hung out as part of the 'British Invasion', travelling with the Beatles on their first tour of America – becoming good friends with John Lennon in the process. Then, in 1972, Baby had become a fixture at the famed Ramport Recording Studios owned by The Who.

The more Mildred spoke of Baby, the more Baby seemed so much like her mother.

With Joanna gone, I stayed at the flat long enough to welcome Baby before heading to Kirsty's.

Mildred had remained at the window all morning waiting for her girl. Mildred was dressed in Levi's, a blouse tied at the waist, showing off her midriff, and rattan wedges. When she finally did arrive, we took the lift to the ground floor to greet her, a new-found energy enabling Mildred to almost run down the front steps of the building. Her excitement at seeing Baby was touching if theatrical. I heard almost nothing from Mildred for the entirety of her daughter's stay.

Nine

Technology

'We've got a situation,' Mildred told me.

I'd decided to get fit that summer, so once reinstalled at the flat after Baby's departure, I was up bright and early to go for a run. It was already warm at eight a.m. The roads in the local neighbourhood were quiet. I'd just run past Luise Rainer's flat on Eaton Square when my mobile rang. I fished the phone out from the pocket of my shorts. It was Mildred. She sounded panicked. She'd obviously not seen the note which I'd left on the side table next to her recliner.

'Darling, where are you?' she asked, her voice high and edgy.

I reminded Mildred that I'd started running in the mornings. She had forgotten. She was still pining for Baby.

'Oh, Orstin, this is awful, darling. It's Dermot Murnaghan, that nice man on the TV – he's disappeared, gone blank and went bang, darling. He's gone and died on me! Oh, it's just terrible! One minute he was there and the next he's blanko, baby.'

A passer-by slowed as he walked past me, undoubtedly worried as I almost shouted to be heard, trying to calm Mildred down, trying to figure out what she was on about. I managed to ascertain that it wasn't Dermot who had expired, but her old 1980s Grundig.

Having thought, when she couldn't find me either in bed or in the shower, that I'd stayed out with perhaps a new woman, Mildred had been forced to call Larry to see if he could fix it.

Once she was a little calmer, Mildred was happy I'd not gone the way of the television and I was at least alive. She couldn't hang on too long as Larry would be with her any minute and she had no make-up on to greet him. The line went dead.

Ten minutes later, I was heading south down Chester Square when my phone rang again. It was Mildred.

Larry had been up to the flat and had now gone again without as much as a cheery 'hello'. She felt he was annoyed with her because she'd told him there was an emergency. For some reason, he hadn't shared her belief that the sudden evaporation of Dermot Murnaghan was worth getting him over to the flat post-haste, still in his white string vest and pyjama bottoms.

She told me he had been groaning and panting as he tried different plug sockets with no luck. The television had officially died.

'I tried with Larry, darling,' she said. 'I offered him a vodka martini but he refused.' She changed her tone. 'Not that I care. Christ, Larry in a vest is hardly a match for Bruce Willis!'

'But it's not much past eight, Cissie,' I shouted. 'How do you manage alcohol at this hour?'

'Practice,' she sniffed – a line she'd heard used by one of her icons, Sir Winston Churchill.

I detected a slight whimper as she hung up. She'd have to say goodbye to yet another appliance she'd purchased with Geoffrey during their halcyon days before all the money ran out.

I was almost back at the flat when the third call came. She'd be unable to cope with a day at home without her telly, so ordered me to pick up my pace and go via Arco (she meant Argos) to buy a new one; nothing too expensive, but something with a decent picture and decent sound. Peter Jones – or 'Pedro Johannes', as she and Geoffrey had called it – on Sloane Square was deemed too expensive.

Back at the flat, she appeared bereft, and moreover anxious that I'd come home without a television. She looked behind me as if I might somehow be hiding one behind my back. I followed her as she grumbled along the hall to the recliner, where she flopped down and pointed to where the television had previously stood. Larry had already, in her words, 'buried it'.

I explained that I'd been without my wallet and didn't now have time to shower, go out again to Argos, come back with a TV, and still get to the office at any decent hour.

I left her thirty minutes later. She had first listened to the news on BBC Radio Four and then, just as I was closing the door, she had located BBC Radio Two, happier to be listening to music rather than *Woman's Hour*.

It was late but still unbearably hot by the time I left work and got to Argos, only to find it was shut. I sheepishly entered the flat to find Mildred in the recliner.

I was hoping she'd enjoy some peace and quiet, even

take advantage of a soap opera-free evening. I thought I could perhaps take her to the Ebury bar.

Instead, Mildred was staring directly at the space on the rug where the Grundig once stood. She was fanning herself with one of the late Victorian ostrich feather fans that had belonged to her mother, part of a collection she'd proudly shown Joanna and me during the Big Clean. She was definitely dressed for the climate, in cut-off denim shorts and the top half of her favourite 'Greek' outfit.

'Oh, there you are, darling!' she said, and turned down the volume on her CD player. 'Listen, I'd forgotten we had these records. Joanna must have tidied them away. I found them in the bureau whilst I was looking for my scrapbooks.'

She pointed beside her to the side table, where she had gathered in a neat pile the CDs she'd obviously hung onto – freebies with her *Daily Express* newspaper.

She tossed me a cardboard CD cover – 'Sixties Summer Hits' – and turned up the sound on the portable CD player balanced on the arm of the recliner.

'Oh, Gawd,' she smiled, 'Who needs *Emmerdale Farm* when there's music to be enjoyed?' She beamed. 'Oh, darling, I've had fun, darling. It's taken my mind off losing my beautiful daughter again.'

Rosebud started making the most peculiar sounds. 'Oh, Orstin, Rosie thinks her Mama's gone crazy, darling. I've been moving around to the groove.'

With that, she clambered to her feet, her toes squeezed into floral fabric wedge flip-flops, and danced a few steps to *You Can't Hurry Love* before she decided it was probably too hot to party.

'Christ, if I carry on having this much fun I'll get me a dizzy spell,' she said, flopping back into the recliner. She paid me closer attention. She was certain I was overheating and therefore suggested she fix me a cool drink while I freshen up. I opted for just water – nonsense, she said, insisting on a vodka martini.

It was only when she stood in the kitchen, mixing our drinks, that it hit her: she had not seen the new television yet. She became cross with me for going to the shops too late, annoyed I'd not taken the loss of her 'old friend' seriously. We argued. Finally, I yielded and promised I'd go to Argos first thing in the morning. She was suspicious.

'You'll be called to the office, and then where will that leave me?'

Then, to my amazement, she decided she'd be joining me at Argos rather than letting me go alone. She was positive that she would be best to judge which TV set would suit her: the shape, the size, the screen.

'Darling, you're forgetting I was in motion pictures. If anyone knows the screen, it's me.'

'And how could I forget you were on screen, Cissie? There's evidence everywhere.' She didn't answer. I decided no further comment was the best course of action.

I stepped into the hall and sent my colleague Marina a text to say I'd be late into the office in the morning. She called me directly after, asking if I could pen an obituary overnight for *King Kong* star Fay Wray, whom she'd heard had just died.

Refreshed, I arrived in the living room in shorts and a T-shirt. Mildred handed me a cocktail, complete with an olive. I took the drink, and she asked that we be friends and clink glasses to seal the deal.

'What shall we toast?' she asked. 'I know – the heat! Oh, I love it!'

After a few sips, I asked Mildred if she'd ever met Fay Wray. She only questioned why I'd dug up 'that old broad'. She was suddenly quiet. I could tell by her expression that she was mulling something over.

'That big ape said he'd make me famous if I allowed him to fool around with me a little,' she said, knocking back her drink. 'Oh, Orstin, what'd you mention him for? Oh, Gawd, I'd forgotten all about him.'

'Cissie, you're telling me that you and King Kong were intimate? Wow, those big hands.' I laughed, as did she. 'Actually, Cissie, I'm only asking about Fay Wray – she's just died.'

'Oh, Gawd, isn't that awful? How old was she?' she said, crossing herself.

Mildred was relieved when I told her Fay Wray had been ninety-seven but asked me not to mention death any more. I would pen Fay's obituary later when she had gone to bed.

As Mildred drained the dregs from her glass, it became clear that the 'ape' she'd referred to was actually the producer Lewis O. Selznick: the bankrupt, ailing, sixty-year-old father of *Gone with the Wind* producer David O. Selznick. He'd promised Mildred some plum parts in films, including her debut in *Bill of Divorcement* with Katharine Hepburn, which was also produced by his son. The condition was that they would 'play around a little'. Mildred agreed; however, Lewis had died before she was able to fully leverage anything from their tryst beyond a couple of bit parts and a test for the role of Ann Darrow in *King Kong*, made famous by Fay Wray.

'I think it was Ginger Rogers who introduced me to Selznick. All I was required to do was scream a lot, that's about all I remember,' said Mildred, on her feet with my glass and hers in hand, headed to the kitchen for a refill.

'Lewis told me the part was mine, but it wasn't. There were the three of us: a brunette – Frances something or other – Fay Wray, and me. I was dark then, too, like Clara Bow. A wardrobe man made us wear dreadful curly wigs. Christ, I looked like Harpo Marx!' she laughed.

Of all her stories, all her close encounters – her near misses, her brushes with fame, her 'nearly, but not quite' moments that could have placed her amongst the greats with whom she brushed shoulders at R.K.O, Metro-Goldwyn-Mayer and Republic Pictures – her audition for *King Kong* was perhaps her most impressive.

She returned with fresh glasses.

'So I wore a curly blonde wig and a sort of ivory evening dress. That night Selznick said the part was mine.'

'He lied to you, Cissie?'

'No, he died!' She roared with laughter. 'Gawd, talk about a near miss – it was a case of "So long, King Kong" and off to the next audition.'

The following morning, I found Mildred dressed, in full make-up, and eating breakfast by eight. As she stared blankly at the void left by the television, she explained her theory that the heat was the reason the television's life had ended. Not wanting to dwell any longer, she dumped her cereal bowl and teacup and saucer amongst last night's washing-up (which she'd promised to do, and hadn't) and the two pairs of tights and grey (formerly white) thong that were hanging off the mixer tap.

Dressed in white slacks (stained with lipstick) and a calamine lotion-coloured blouse accessorised with a fringed scarf, Panama hat, and Sunnie Mann shades, she hurried me down Ebury Street towards Victoria Street and Argos.

She was not overly impressed with the décor. The lighting was too dim for her to be able to see which television sets were available in the Argos brochure. After complaining to the staff, an employee by the name of Tyrone located a torch for her. Mildred immediately asked him if he was named after the actor Tyrone Power. He was not, as it turned out. Tyrone told us he'd been named after a boyfriend of his mother's. Puzzled and inquisitive, Mildred asked if the boyfriend was his father. He shrugged his shoulders.

'Oh, you poor child,' she said, crossing herself. Tyrone left us to peruse the audio section.

'Can I help you?' asked a sales assistant called Chanéqua, her name clearly printed on the badge fastened under the collar of her staff uniform.

Undoubtedly Chanéqua had heard Mildred complaining loudly that she'd like to 'test drive' the television sets before making such a huge purchase. Mildred was not all that impressed with Chanéqua, even though it was not her fault that the employees couldn't do what Mildred demanded: open just one or two boxes, plug in the TVs, and find Mildred a chair so she could watch and listen instore before handing over a couple of hundred pounds.

Tyrone reappeared; he was willing to demonstrate one of the sets in the catalogue and asked if she'd like to step over to where he'd plugged it in already. Mildred brushed past Chanéqua.

'Tyrone, darling, you've got to do something about the lights. A doctor told me once it's dangerous to watch the television in the dark,' scolded Mildred.

'It ain't dark,' laughed Chanéqua. 'It's August, lady, and it's sunny outside.'

At this point, I feared I was never going to make it to the office.

Tyrone pulled across a standard lamp and plugged in another spotlight so Mildred could view the television in the way that satisfied her needs. There was a film on one of the channels he flicked to: *Pal Joey* with Frank Sinatra and Rita Hayworth. Mildred ordered Tyrone, 'Stop right there!'

'Kids,' she said to Tyrone, to Chanéqua, who was definitely intrigued by Mildred, and to another employee, a man of about fifty-five who had walked over, 'when I was starting out in motion pictures, that woman and I were friends. Oh, Rita Hayworth was Rita Cansino back then: the Brooklyn-born daughter of a Mexican dance teacher!'

'What's your name, madam?' asked Tyrone.

'Oh, Mildred Shay – Walter Winchell crowned me "Pocket Venus". You've heard of me, of course.'

A grinning Tyrone, a man in a suit, and two further customers stood around Mildred and listened. The older man told Mildred that his 'old mum' was named after Rita Hayworth and to his mind was 'just as much of a knockout'. She looked him up and down.

'Is that so, darling?' she said, her tone sarcastic.

Tyrone found her a seat.

'Christ, she didn't look like that back then!' said Mildred, watching Rita and Sinatra together. 'She had a very low brow that the studio 'sorted' with tweezers,' she laughed. 'Oh, and Rita was shy. We shared the billing on one of those publicity drives. "Oh, Mildred," she'd say, "Mildred, I'm too scared to speak," so yours truly ran the whole darn outfit!'

'Lady,' said Chanéqua, whom Mildred had asked to fetch her a glass of water, 'that don't surprise me one bit, honey!'

Mildred signed six autographs before we left. Tyrone hailed us a taxi and helped me into the cab with the new TV in a box. At the other end, I managed to get it from the taxi to the lift and into the flat. I left Mildred to unpack it.

In the hurry to get to work that morning, I accidentally left my mobile on my bed. When I arrived home much later, Mildred was incandescent with rage. I wanted to laugh at her get-up (a baby-blue bathing costume) but she was in such a state that laughter was off limits.

Not being able to get hold of me all day, she'd had to get Larry back up to the flat to set up the television. To her horror, the remote hadn't been in the box. She'd have to miss more *Family Affairs, Emmerdale Farm, Coronation Street,* and *Eastenders.* She slouched off to her bedroom like a grumpy teenager. She soon surfaced when she smelt dinner – spinach and salmon flan with new potatoes.

Despite the new television being unusable, Mildred wouldn't join me at the dining table and opted instead to remain in the recliner. Still moody, I decided to slip on one of her CDs to break the deathly silence – Marilyn Monroe singing *Some Like It Hot.*

'Did I ever tell you I knew Marilyn?' asked Mildred. 'She wasn't all that gorgeous – not like Hedy Lamarr.'

Mildred and Geoffrey had been friends with Bobby Kennedy and had known JFK, although not intimately. They were all part of a larger group invited to cocktail parties at Peter Lawford's Beverly Hills home. Mildred recalled it was at one such 'do' that Bobby had introduced her to Marilyn.

'The voice was all a con,' she grumbled, her mouth full of food. 'I heard her speak to Bobby and she sounded normal – everything she did was for effect. Christ, I can't stand show-offs!'

For the remainder of that evening, Mildred recounted one Hollywood yarn after another, only breaking away from film royalty with an extraordinary tale of herself, Adeline, and her parents talking to Queen Mary at a Buckingham Palace reception during the late 1940s. That conversation had centred on whether Joseph Shay could recommend a reputable company who would install air conditioning at her official residence, Marlborough House. After one of the coldest winters on record and an extremely wet spring, by June 1948 the heat was causing tarmac to melt and even the most respectable in society to wilt.

'My perfectly brilliant Daddy called the head of Fedders, who was one of his clients, and arranged for their latest model to be wrapped and shipped to the attention of Her Majesty at Marlborough House. Oh, she was really grateful, I mean blown away, darling, by Daddy's thoughtfulness. I have a letter someplace from her Private Secretary – Christ, Daddy saved her life! He shoulda gotten a knighthood!'

Mildred kicked back the footrest and got up from the recliner. 'I'm gonna find that letter.'

She headed to the make-up room. I heard her pulling open drawers. She re-materialised with a stack of letters, and tossed some onto my lap, asking that I read them back to her. Before I could get started, however, she picked up one which had dropped to the floor. It was from the film director Eddie Sutherland. She started reading the contents to me. 'Well, whaddya know. I had forgotten all about him!'

Queen Mary had gone cold as, distracted, Mildred recalled her dates with Sutherland, with Walter Pidgeon, with Dick Arlen, and half a dozen other Hollywood men.

At quarter to twelve she decided to call it a night.

'You know what,' shouted Mildred, to be heard through the closed bathroom door, 'I wonder if I can't get Daddy a posthumous knighthood. I bet they're all lying in their beds at the Palace tonight as cool as cucumbers! God, you've got to hand it to my father, he was incomparable to anyone else on the planet.'

She decided to leave at the same time as me the next morning. She was going back to have it out with 'that female' at Argos. Mildred felt sure Chanéqua didn't like her – surely jealous, probably of all the male attention she had received yesterday.

'I've seen it my entire life, darling,' she sniffed as she checked her reflection in the Argos shop window. She toyed with her hair as she pouted back at herself. 'That's why I can't stand females.'

Mildred beamed as she spied Tyrone on the other side of the glass. She gave him a wave before proceeding to unfasten a further button on her already gaping blouse.

'Hello, Pocket Rocket,' said Tyrone as he opened the doors.

I happily left her in his capable hands.

Later that day I discovered a voice message on my mobile. Mildred came away from Argos minus the remote; she'd been so carried away with Tyrone that she'd forgotten what she went in for. Unable to walk back unaided, she asked that I call by after work to collect it.

I was about the leave the office when Mildred called again. She'd managed to find the number for 'Arco' herself and had spoken to Tyrone. He had offered to hand-deliver it.

'Darling,' she giggled, 'Don't hurry home, I'm gonna get Tyrone to tune me in and, as he's a fan, show him *Valentino*.'

I suggested perhaps it would be unwise, as she didn't know him all that well.

'Well, darling, that's just the thing. I'm gonna get to

know him better!' she said, punctuating her goodbye with that now very familiar giggle.

* * *

If having to say goodbye to the television hadn't been enough, saying goodbye to a second old friend was heart-breaking.

Clean as we might, the old fridge retained a queer chemical smell, so Joanna and I ordered a new one and arranged to have the old one dumped. Howard had helped me to move it into the hall to await the removal team. Mildred stroked it every time she passed it from that moment until its final exit. She would whimper, 'How I'll miss you, old friend.' Mildred demanded to be present when two men from the council came to collect it.

At nine-thirty in the morning there was a knock at the front door: the removal men. Mildred, wearing a black mini-skirt, woollen tights, and black cocktail hat, insisted on answering it, and wept as she did so.

Mildred accompanied her Kelvinator on its final journey as it was rolled along the hall on a trolley. With Mildred leading the way, the procession was painfully slow. Mildred couldn't resist pointing out the famous people in pictures frames whom she and Geoffrey had once entertained.

I'd suggested before the men arrived that it would be best if her farewell were a quick one, the men undoubt-edly being busy. But Mildred insisted she needed more time. I stood on the other side of the front door with

Mildred clinging onto me. 'Goodbye, old friend,' she cried as the lift doors closed on the two bewildered men and the Kelvinator. With that, another survivor from her days of abundance had gone for good.

Watch with Mother:
Mildred on Lillian Shay's
knee. 1913

Racket Ready: Mildred
clowns around flanked
by her beloved German
Großmutter and Grossvater
and an aunt. Cedarhurst,
New York. 1918.

On tour: Mildred and mother with her dear sister Adeline. Vichy, France, circa 1926.

It's Mildred on the dance floor: (left) Mildred ballet pose circa 1925. *"Mother said I was too fat to dance"*.

Knock it off: Eager to
grow up fast, Mildred
lied about her age to
obtain a drivers license.

Shay Style: Proud father
Joseph A. Shay with his
fashionable family; Lillian,
Mildred and Adeline.

Vamp it up: Mildred
tries out a new femme
fatale look as Hollywood
beckons (1931).

On a Hollywood High: TOP Mildred as Madame Chee-Chee between Alan Ladd and Thurston Hall in 'In Old Missouri' (1940). LEFT with her Balalaika (1939) co-star Nelson Eddy. ABOVE At the Gilmore Stadium with Cary Grant on a morale boosting War Bonds drive, 1944.

Hair Style of The Women at M.G.M.

This Woman's Work: TOP Mildred Shay as Helené, Crystal Allen (played by Joan Crawford) French maid in George Cukor's 'The Women' (1939). LEFT In uniform for the Gene Autry vehicle 'Ride Tenderfoot Ride' (1940). BELOW Perky 'Pocket Venus' at a Hollywood party 1938.

Third time lucky: TOP LEFT: Mildred wearing famed 'Made in England' suit by Sir Hardy Amies flanked by husband Geoffrey Steele and actors John Garfield and Geraldine Fitzgerald. TOP: Back in Hollywood after the end of WWII. CENTRE LEFT: Dressed to impress: Academy Awards dinner, Hollywood, 1947. BOTTOM LEFT: Mildred wears her favourite gold and seed-pearl necklace once owned by Princess Eugenie of France. ABOVE: Baby makes three: Christening party, St. Michael's Church, Chester Square, London, May 1950.

TOP LEFT: All aboard: Mildred wears a re-fashioned 1940s gown by Adrian to go as a French tart and Geoffrey as a cowboy to the Captain's cocktail party, Cunard 1982. TOP CENTRE: Hello Daddy: Mildred and her cherished father Joseph A. Shay, circa 1950. TOP RIGHT: Bathing Beauty: Mildred in her favourite powder-blue swimming costume. This was the outfit she wore when I bid her farewell for the last time in October 2005. BELOW: Last tango: "Gay or not, we had a moment in the jon". Mildred gazes at Rudolph Nureyev (Ken Russell's 'Valentino' 1977).

TOP LEFT: The Last Picture Show: Mildred with her 'bricks', 2003. ABOVE: Max Factor ready: Preparing for her close-up; The Cavalry & Guards Club, 2004. CENTRE LEFT: The Fab Four: Austin and Joanna's wedding day, September 2005. LEFT: Triangle of trust: Mildred kisses the bride, St. Paul's Church, Parkend, Gloucestershire, 2005. BOTTOM LEFT: Mildred and me in 2003.

Ten

The Interview

*H*oward's touting Mildred around town had paid off: she was offered a full-page interview feature in *The Observer*. Mildred disliked the paper for being too 'left'; however, she swallowed her pride and settled a date. Only afterwards did Mildred ring Howard at work, stipulating that in return for giving 'that newspaper' a 'Mildred Shay exclusive' she should be taken out to lunch for the interview, in the same way Hedda Hopper and Walter Winchell took her to the Brown Derby or Chasen's for 'a marvellous martini whilst we all had a lovely chat'.

When I got home that night, Mildred was rather vexed. There would be no lunch as there wasn't the budget for it. She was hesitating about whether to do the interview at all. I told her that the paper, particularly the weekend supplement magazine for which the interview was intended, was very popular. She relented and phoned Howard to say she'd do it – unbeknownst to her, he had booked the interview regardless.

The day arrived.

The door to the make-up room was ajar. Inside, Mildred stood facing herself in the mirror. She played with her diamond and platinum bracelets and twisted on a giant diamond ring and an emerald cluster over a gnarled index finger. She called out to me that her mother would never have been so gauche as to wear diamonds before six, and never ever wore pearls after sunset.

'Mother!' she said, louder, to her own reflection. 'Go screw yourself!'

Mildred completed the look with another ring, an opal surrounded by diamonds, and a giant twenty-four-carat gold emblem of Geoffrey's regiment, The Blues and Royals, pinned to her left lapel.

'Oh shit!' she said aloud. 'I've everything but money.' With that, she added a diamond necklace.

In the living room, she flopped in the recliner and awaited the press.

The buzzer went. 'Oh, God, that's the newspaper people and I look a mess,' she cried. 'You go and get some refreshments ready, Orstin. I'm going to greet them. I don't want the newspapers to think I'm some old crone and can't open the door myself.'

With that, Mildred wiggled past me into the hall and picked up the entry phone. 'Come up and see me some time,' she said playfully, mimicking her old nemesis Mae West. And then louder: 'Come up, come up!'

Up indeed. Mildred had woken me shuffling about the flat that morning shortly after five-thirty. By seven, Joanna (back in London) and I had been given a full dress rehearsal.

Mildred had become completely relaxed in Joanna's and my presence now. She wasn't bothered by Joanna or me seeing her naked. That morning, the day of the newspaper interview, Mildred had left the bathroom in her birthday suit (and shower cap), greeting me with a cheery, 'Oh, hello, Orstin, dear!'

For Mildred, talking was no problem, but being photographed was. Mildred couldn't recall the last time she'd sat for a professional photographer. She was nervous.

The outfit had been carefully planned and pressed by Joanna days before; Joanna also managed to talk Mildred out of wearing the ancient Pucci, the Hartnell, or the Hardy Amies. Instead, she convinced Mildred to embrace something a bit more twenty-first century: a smart grey tweed-style fitted jacket, purchased by Howard from House of Fraser, worn with black slacks and a diamante-studded top, both from Primark, finished off with a pair of black patent leather wedges. Mildred had waited for half a lifetime to face the camera again, and yet with Joanna's styling, she looked modern – she was even wearing a little less panstick.

Her fragrance too had been updated: from Giorgio Beverly Hills to Jo Malone. Mildred dowsed herself in Wild Fig & Cassis – 'for a wild woman', she said, before she tossed the bottle through the open door in the direction of her bed. Rosebud scampered into the bedroom just as Mildred shut the door. Rosebud wanted to be alone; Mildred never wanted to be alone again.

The journalists finally arrived.

As it was the working week, I insisted we drink tea. I set up a tray with her best china. The kettle had boiled twice and still Mildred held her captives by the front door, telling tales about her friends in the photographs.

'Darlings, this is me with Duncan Renaldo…Oh, Gawd, whatcha mean you've never heard of him? He was the Cisco Kid! Nearly killed his co-star Edwina Booth once. Duncan was a big star!'

She continued, 'This is me with Nelson Eddy, he and I would knit in Joan Crawford's Winnebago. He had such soft hands, and my dears, he never made a pass…' As she talked I detected the party edging at a snail's pace towards the living room.

'This is Natalie Wood. A brat! That's Alfred Hitch-cock, of course. I was with Hitch the night Bobby Kennedy was killed…' She stopped. 'No, that's wrong…I was with Bobby Kennedy himself when he was shot, I think. No matter…And this is me with Alan Ladd. Married or not, he was crazy about me, I mean madly in love with me – obsessed…' She waited a heartbeat. 'Oh, okay, you've dragged it outta me. Yes, we had an affair. I tell you, for a little guy he was big down there,' she giggled.

I peeked around the kitchen door. The visitors were almost free; but they seemed genuinely impressed – as I had been – by her gallery of movie stars, albeit ones who were mostly forgotten. In full throttle now, Mildred bounced towards me, almost dancing as she punched the air. The younger of two males commented on her moves.

'Oh, darling, I'm a working actress and a swingin' chick,' she said over her shoulder as she winked at me.

I detected surprise in the man's voice.

'Oh, yes, my dear, I've got an agent. I'm ready for work,' she squealed.

'Oh, hi,' said the young man to me as he looked into the kitchen. Mildred crept up behind him. He jumped. He was handsome, raven-haired, and rugged. Mildred cooed as she introduced him: 'Orstin, this is my Tom.' Tom was joined by another man, Henry, and a woman in her thirties. Mildred was dismissive of Maggie until Maggie revealed that she was the one conducting the interview.

'Oh, is that so?' said Mildred, looking her up and down. 'A female interviewer. Well, I suppose I got on marvellously with Hedda and Louella!'

'I had a great friend called Maggie. Maggie Roach. She was the daughter of Hal Roach, who teamed Laurel with Hardy. Maggie and I were so close and then she wanted to get closer! Oh, yes, Maggie liked girls! I mean, I'm not my own type.' Mildred left this Maggie dumbstruck.

'Let's put on some lights,' said Mildred as the party reached the living room. I followed with the tray of tea.

'Oh, now, this is my boyfriend,' laughed Mildred.

'Hi, I'm Austin. I'm Mildred's friend.' The group all shook hands with me. 'She assured me she'll keep it clean.'

'Yeah, and it's too bad, but he won't sleep with me.'

The visitors laughed.

'She's hilarious,' said Tom.

'She's performing for you all – there's a new house in the theatre tonight!' I replied with a wry smile as I served the tea and then returned to the kitchen to make a coffee for Maggie.

I listened as Mildred mentioned her 'dearest friends':

Glenn Ford, Victor Mature, Bob Hope. 'I have so many friends – and some of them are still above ground!' she joked.

Mildred held court from her recliner – delighted that the conversation focused purely on her. After an hour, tea made way for vodka martinis. On her feet, Mildred turned barman – mixing and stirring as she spoke.

'Well, Cary Grant had such a very close friendship with Randolph Scott...the MGM school house with its white picket fence was a hotbed of debauchery...' Mildred poured her own cocktail first. 'I never drank when I was in Hollywood,' she said, before taking a sip and burping. 'I never wanted to miss anything, and besides, I didn't much care for alcohol anyways.'

'You've made up for it now,' I called, returning to the kitchen.

'You are awful,' she screamed. 'That's ten bucks from your wages this week!'

I heard Mildred tell the visitors more about me.

'He's engaged to be married, unfortunately – and to a country girl. But she's quite charming, apart from the fact she's thinking about turning vegetarian! And she won't wear my furs!'

'I'm a vegetarian too,' said Maggie.

'Oh, shit!' said Mildred, and turned to me as I walked back into the room. 'Orstin! We've got another one! Vegetarians! I can't stand it. Humans need iron and blood to survive,' said Mildred. 'I played a vegan in *The Wolvercote Tongue* – an episode of *Inspector Morse* – I can't stand the idea of it,' said Mildred, and pretended to vomit. 'But,' she said, her tone triumphant, 'critics said I was more boorish than John Thaw...God, I was good in that. Oh, but vegetarians! Please!'

Rather like Joanna, Maggie had seemingly figured out pretty quickly that it was best not to react. Instead, she lowered her gaze and lifted her handbag onto her lap. She retrieved a notepad.

Mildred broke the awkward pause. 'Oh, God,' she said, as she grabbed hold of my hand. 'Listen, my boyfriend here is a newspaper man. I hate to say it, but this man writes obituaries for a living. I've banned him from including my name in any of them.'

'Who do you write for?' asked Henry.

'*The Daily Telegraph.*'

'I love the *Telegraph*'s obituaries,' replied Henry. Tom and Maggie agreed, and for a few moments we all – apart from Mildred – discussed what made a really good obit.

Mildred interrupted. 'Well, isn't this afternoon about me?' she laughed sarcastically, while she wobbled back to the recliner. I knew how she hated any mention of death. 'Let's not talk about obituaries anymore.' She looked up at the ceiling. 'Lord, don't listen. I'm not going anywhere yet.'

She finished her cocktail, handed me her glass, and indicated that she'd like a refill. Only Maggie joined Mildred for round two (Mildred's third).

I took the glass and mixed my own martini for Mildred – a sniff of vodka with a hefty top-up of tap water.

From the kitchen, I heard the conversation. Mildred had started to talk with Maggie. 'Darling, how long have you worked in newspapers?'

'Oh, ten years, and three on *The Observer*.'

'You married, dear?' asked Mildred.

'No, I have a partner,' replied Maggie.

'That's nice, dear,' said Mildred, as she took her drink from me.

Back in the kitchen, I heard Mildred continue with the niceties. I knew she hated the term 'partner'. I knew she couldn't care less about Maggie. It was Tom that she liked. I'd noticed how Mildred offered only Tom a Ritz cracker from her best Spode hors-d'ouvre plate, whilst she made the others fend for themselves. I had seen how, when Maggie and Henry spoke, she talked over them to discover if Tom was hitched. How flirtatious she became when he told her he was single. Mildred complimented Tom on how he wore his hair and laughed when he told her that his sister cut it.

'Oh, that's so sweet, honey,' she said, placing her diamond-encrusted hand on his knee. 'Is your sister a trained hairdresser?'

'Yeah, and she does tattoos,' said Tom as he finished his drink.

'How marvellous,' smirked Mildred, who hated tattoos with a passion. 'Oh, Tom, do you know who cut my hair? It was Sydney Guillaroff! He was Metro's most famous hairdresser. He worked on Judy Garland, Joan Crawford, and that lofty streak of piss – oh, yes, Ros Russell.' I laughed at Mildred's cheap jibe at Russell, with whom she'd fallen out after Ros caught Mildred in a clinch with her husband Freddie Brisson.

'Sydney told me to wear my hair off my face and never to do bangs. Well…' she laughed saucily and then smiled at Tom '…Well, those kinda bangs anyway. He knew about the other bangs I had.' She laughed again, as did Tom – his more of a nervous titter.

I could tell Tom was becoming somewhat embarrassed, just as I had the first time she and I had met. Unaware of how much was too much, she continued with more 'sauce'.

Mildred talked and talked; however, she became increasingly vague with dates and facts. Rather than listen to Maggie, Mildred watched Tom unpack and fix the lighting for the photo shoot.

'How old do you think I am?' she asked as he held a reading light in front of her face.

Tom's eyes darted from Mildred's to mine, to Maggie's, and back to Mildred's. He took a step back. 'Well, I used to be a nurse so this should be easy,' he said confidently. 'About ninety.'

'Oh, shit!' said Mildred. 'You don't pull any punches, do you? I mean…shit!'

Maggie turned to a fresh page in her notepad. 'Hey, listen, Austin, can I ask you to take a seat and join us? I think you'll be able to fill in some gaps where Mildred might forget. Mildred lost track of some details when I spoke to her on the phone last week. She seemed to get confused.'

Mildred chimed in, 'Well, Maggie, dear, why don't we let you ask Orstin all the questions, and then Mildred and her senility may just muster up enough brain cells to help out with the leftovers.'

Maggie was stunned. 'I'm not being rude – I just want it to be absolutely right,' she said, staring at Mildred and then at me. 'Austin, can you help here?' Her tone was increasingly desperate.

'Hey, Mildred, Maggie only wants it to be just right,' I said.

Mildred blanked Maggie and then, taking a hearty gulp of liquor, smiled before sending a sideways scowl towards Maggie. She snarled, 'Well, isn't that thoughtful of her, darling.'

Trying to get back on track, Maggie commented on how beautiful Mildred had been as she looked over at some of the photographs of her on the windowsill.

'Miss Shay, you were so beautiful in these photos. Did you model before you started in films?' said Maggie, trying for a new angle.

'Model!' Mildred threw her head back and laughed. 'My dear Maggie, my wonderful father Joseph A. Shay was a big mokey-moke Supreme U.S. attorney who worked on some of the biggest cases in American history, like the Becker murder trials. We wintered in Palm Beach and had a home that covered an entire block in Cederhurst, New York. We travelled all over Europe. I was educated at a Swiss school for genteel ladies in Lausanne. When I was fourteen, Daddy brought my younger sister Adeline and me to London on the Queen Mary. We had a suite each. My maid had been a countess at the Romanoff court in St. Petersburg. So, darling, to answer your question, no, I wasn't a model.'

'Oh, Miss Shay, how glamorous!' said Maggie, and her enthusiasm, like Joanna's on occasions, was a little fake, worn down by the enormity of Mildred.

'Glamorous? I never gave it a thought,' Mildred retorted.

Mildred asked that Maggie get up and fetch a photo of Baby from the windowsill. 'Now, Baby, she's the model,' said Mildred, examining a glossy photograph of Baby from the sixties. 'My daughter was feted as the American Twiggy. Oh, my dear Maggie, Baby was just as brilliant as can be, and so clever! I tell you, Baby has the same IQ as Einstein…Did I mention already that I met Einstein?'

Mildred handed the photo back to Maggie. 'Take a closer look, dear,' she insisted. 'Oh, Baby was so pretty. She had a perfectly symmetrical face…Oh, Baby could have married Prince Charles! The Queen and I shared the same doctor, Sir William Gilliatt, so we were real close. I had Baby at the hospital by caesarean. My perfectly marvellous Daddy found the best nurses for his special baby-girl.' Mildred pointed at a sepia-toned photo of a small child wearing a bonnet and fur collar.

'That's me,' she smiled. 'See, I wore fur even then – shit! I can't stand these fruit-loops that only wanna eat vegetables!'

'Mildred, everyone's entitled to their own opinions,' I said.

'Sure, darling, I'm a proud American – it's the land of the free!' said Mildred with a hiccup.

Maggie huffed but otherwise remained silent. She checked her wristwatch. I felt very soon she might just pack up and leave altogether.

Mildred forced the photo of Baby onto Tom. 'They

met in the park: Prince Charles with his nanny, Nanny Lightfoot, and my Baby with her nanny.'

Composing herself, Maggie suggested that Baby and Prince Charles had been far too young to think about such things.

'Baby was no normal child. She could have been a quantum physicist,' said Mildred proudly. 'Anyways, Baby rebuked Prince Charles' advances – she thought his ears were too big!'

'Imagine it, Mildred,' I said. 'Baby as Queen and you as the Queen Mother!'

'Wouldn't that have been something?' laughed Mildred.

'Yes indeed,' said Maggie, with more than a hint of sarcasm.

Mildred asked that I hand Tom and Henry her scrapbooks from a purple zip-up attaché case beside the recliner. Both started to flick through the pages. Maggie peered over.

'I have to say, Miss Shay, I wasn't very familiar with your name, but I can see you were very pretty,' she said. 'And your life and that of your family, so intertwined with so many people of note.'

Maggie asked Tom to pass her a stack of photos he'd been studying. 'Oh, lovely, just lovely!'

Mildred grabbed a cracker, snapped it between her painted talons, and with a wry smile said, ever so politely, 'Next question, Maggie.'

Maggie reverted to asking questions about whom Mildred had known in Hollywood. Mildred took this as a query about whom she'd slept with and reeled off a long list of her conquests.

'Victor Mature just laid there and I had to provide all the action. That manly image he portrayed in *Samson and Delilah* was all phoney. My friend Hedy Lamarr told me he was a great big sissy. I didn't know much about that!' She smacked her hand on her knee like a seasoned cowgirl and beamed. 'All I know is Victor was big!'

Mildred recalled how she thought David Manners, the star of her first film, *Bill of Divorcement*, 'a livin' doll', whereas their co-star Katharine Hepburn had been 'just awful'.

There were moments when Tom laughed out loud. This thrilled Mildred. 'Oh, you must think I'm a raunchy old broad,' she laughed. I realised that the booze, even in its watered-down state, was kicking in. 'Oh, Maggie, dear, you asked me about Hepburn. She had that annoying voice and yes, she was talented, but I found her very pushy.'

Mildred stopped dead. Maggie raised her head.

'In case you haven't guessed, I prefer men,' smirked Mildred.

'Oh, I guessed,' said Maggie.

'Mildred,' she added, 'did you party much?'

'I went to the Cocoanut Grove a lot on dates. I met that vamp actress there, Pola Negri. I thought her scary and I swear she tried to hit on me. I can't stand lesbians. God, all that woman on woman stuff.' Mildred pulled a face and pretended to throw up. When Mildred went on a little too much about her distrust of lesbians, I cut in.

'Mildred, you saw Bing Crosby when he was with The Rhythm Boys, didn't you?'

'Yep,' said Mildred, but she was still on her lesbian tirade. 'I had a Hungarian friend once. I had no idea she was gay. God, when I think we shared a bed together. I love gay men and –'

'Mildred,' I chimed in, 'tell them about Errol Flynn.'

Of all her stories, Mildred was able to shine most triumphantly in the face of adversity when telling this tale. There were several versions of the Flynn fable. I'd heard them all: the brash, the bold, and the not so beautiful.

Maggie moved closer to the edge of her seat. It was the first time I'd truly seen her interested. Tom and Henry, who had completed the set-up, returned to the sofa.

'Oh, it's too awful, I couldn't,' said Mildred, and beamed at me.

'I understand,' said Maggie. 'Listen, if it's too difficult…' Mildred didn't allow Maggie to finish her sentence before starting the story.

All eyes were on Mildred – aside from mine. I left her to her fresh audience. I'd done my bit. I'd introduced the star act and I could head back to the wings.

I opened the back door and lit a cigarette. I pulled my mobile from my pocket and called Joanna. It went to voicemail. I pulled the wooden stool onto the balcony and stared out onto Ebury Street below. Even now, the only noise I could hear was Mildred.

'He tried to rape me!' she shouted. 'At first, I was determined to play hard to get, but he was a big handsome brute!'

I heard Mildred recount more and more sleaze. I realised she'd played hard to get for the journalists, too, but she was finally putty in Maggie's hands.

I got up and headed back to the living room. I was suddenly anxious that this was a newspaper interview and she was putting herself out there, all her extreme dislikes at full volume. Outrageous, yes, but as I'd come to discover, she wasn't malicious. She rarely actually meant it; it was just that, for years, being outrageous, whether in church or at the chemist, had been the only way to be noticed.

I lingered in the living room doorway. Maggie was now the most eager I'd seen her, coaxing more and more out of Mildred.

At this point quite pissed, Mildred told them how she had flirted with Errol, her friends who were sitting with her feverishly guzzling the champagne he'd bought her. Mildred would drink only milk.

'Mr Flynn suggested I clear whatever engagements I had, as a night together would surely take precedence. So he fixed it that he'd come for me the next night at six. He kissed my hand. Everyone at Ciro's that night was watching us.'

'How did he know where to pick you up?' asked Henry.

'If you were anybody you stayed at the Garden of Allah,' said Mildred.

'Naturally you stayed there?' asked Maggie.

'Naturally,' said Mildred.

As Mildred continued, I was reminded of what her mother and Adeline had called her; how Adeline had felt Mildred slept her way around Hollywood. How Mildred had rebuked the females in her family for being jealous of her. Later, however, she told me she did all of it - the hijinks, the chasing, the bed-hopping, and the movies - to bring light to her life, which since the death of her brother Arnold had seen only darkness and despair.

I felt uncomfortable. I returned to the kitchen to fill a glass of water and took it to Mildred. A vain attempt to try and sober her up, to get her to think about where she was going with this version of the story, which was more outrageous than any I'd heard previously.

By that point, Mildred was in Errol Flynn's apartment. I knew the crescendo was coming.

Maggie was scribbling feverishly. Mildred spoke of Errol standing before her in little else but sock garters and an open dress shirt. With her hands, Mildred demonstrated (to Tom in particular) how his manhood grew and grew as he started rubbing it.

'I screamed!' Mildred was screaming now. She told them how he couldn't quite get the shirt free, how it flapped like a white flag about his wrist. 'He used the other hand to masturbate,' she said.

Mildred remembered she ran from behind the chair to behind a standard lamp, knocking the shade from the frame as she tried to run away. 'Errol Flynn blocked any escape as he continued to rub his penis.' Mildred laughed as she told us how she kept shouting 'no'.

She described in minute detail the shape of Flynn's penis, how he dipped his thumb into Mildred's glass of milk and rubbed it, while with the other hand playing with his 'bulbous low-hanging balls'. 'It was completely up and rigid-like, pointing towards the ceiling,' she said with a chortle.

Maggie sat shaking her head in disbelief. I wasn't sure whether she was more aghast at Errol Flynn's behaviour or at Mildred's breezy retelling of the story. I had had the same reaction myself.

Coming to the final act, Mildred's voice darkened. She told us how Flynn suddenly made a dive for her and managed to catch her wrist. Mildred had screamed. She was on her feet now. She demonstrated how the scene unfolded, screaming again.

I heard Rosebud meowing loudly from Mildred's bedroom. Maggie, Tom, and Henry were all still on the edge of their seats. Mildred was somehow towering above them and pulled open her top slightly to illustrate the struggle.

She recalled how the standard lamp had crashed to the ground, how the bulb had smashed into a 'thousand pieces' on the parquet floor. With one swoop, Flynn had grabbed Mildred and thrown her onto the sofa. He had jumped on top of her and started pulling at the hem of her dress.

Mildred said she thumped his smooth chest with her fists and scratched him with her nails. Flynn had grabbed both her hands and held them over her head.

Mildred flopped into the recliner, reliving the moment: she punched the air above her to demonstrate how she had tried to wriggle free under his enormous weight. While trying to part Mildred's legs, Flynn had ripped and then pulled down her stockings. Her shoes had been lost as she had frantically kicked for freedom. Mildred had felt his hand inside her underwear and had cried even louder.

With her voice now even higher, Mildred told us all how she had started to scream louder. Flynn had let go of her hands so he could cover her mouth. Mildred sank her teeth in. Flynn had yelled out just once and then stopped. Mildred had continued to try to free herself and then, after a few minutes, realised that Flynn wasn't trying to force himself on her anymore. Instead, he was simply looking down at her and laughing.

Mildred, sitting on the arm of the recliner, demonstrated to Tom how she had silenced Errol Flynn when she gave him a hard slap. But with just four or five quick tugs Flynn ejaculated over her. She screamed now with jubilation as the story came to a close, but not before she gave a disgusted look as she remembered how he had shaken the last remaining drops of semen from his shrinking penis. She grimaced as she recalled how he had proceeded to wipe his manhood clean on her gown.

'He let me go free. I locked myself in the bathroom,' she told us. 'I screamed from behind the locked door, 'Errol, call me a cab.' I had my gown soaking in the tub, rubbing out the mess with soap and water.'

Mildred had waited until the taxi arrived. With her gown over her arm, she retrieved her fur coat. Errol had stood by the apartment door, dressed in a bathrobe, with her tiny shoes in one hand and her pocketbook in the other. Mildred snatched both from him and then turned and ran.

'You went home then?' asked Henry.

'I couldn't – Mother would still be up,' she said. Mildred had instead ordered the cab to drive her to the

Hollywood Hills, where she sat on a large stone, waiting for the sun to come up and dry her gown.

Mildred had returned to Allah, darted around the back of the bungalow and climbed through her open bedroom window. She had hidden her gown in the back of her wardrobe, combed her hair, and, donning a bathrobe, walked into the small breakfast room and greeted her mother.

Maggie asked why Mildred felt she couldn't confide in her mother. Mildred bawled, 'Mother didn't do 'the birds and the bees' talk. Mother said if one should feel an urge then one should take ether.'

'Didn't it cross your mind to go to the police?' asked Tom.

'Errol Flynn was friends with the cops,' said Mildred.

'Did you ever see Errol Flynn again?' asked Tom.

'Yes, about five years later. He asked me to marry him. He told me that he found me 'spunky',' sniffed Mildred.

After downing her last drink of the afternoon, Mildred rose gingerly, steadied herself, and walked out of the room. The living room fell silent. Maggie was still writing. I peered over her shoulder.

'It's her best story,' I confided in Maggie. Mildred had somehow confused the seriousness of what happened. She had transformed the attempted rape into a weird badge of honour, as if her association with Flynn elevated her own celebrity.

Maggie said the piece would be honest. I asked that it be kind.

Mildred stepped back into the room like an actress returning for an encore. She looked Tom straight in the eye, smiled, and, as she took her place, laughed: 'Mr DeMille, I'm ready for my close-up.'

The camera clicked once, twice, three times. The flash ricocheted off her face and Mildred, silent now, performed for the camera, lifting her chin a little, just like George Cukor had taught her seventy years before. Keeping her eyes wide, if a little seductive, she smiled.

Henry interjected with a 'great' and a 'wonderful, Mildred'. But somehow the air was tainted by her story; partly a sense of grief for what she had gone through and partly a sense of astonishment that she was happy to retell it with such cheer.

'When will the piece go to print?' I asked Maggie, as Mildred spoke with Tom.

'Oh, soon. I think the editor will love her. I find her confusing and complex,' said Maggie. She gathered her notebook and pens together. I fetched her coat from the cedar chest in the hall.

Mildred walked her guests to the front door, where she said her goodbyes.

Maggie spied a photograph of Errol Flynn on the wall amongst the glitterati. She said nothing to Mildred, but she asked me why she had his photo after what he'd done. I told her what Mildred had told me: 'It's part of her Hollywood story.'

'That's truly bizarre,' said Maggie.

'It's fame by association,' I explained.

Having closed the door on the team from *The Observer*, Mildred asked that I fetch her an aspirin. Certain she had a hangover looming, she disappeared into her bedroom with a glass of water and pills.

Joanna was home and we were making dinner when Mildred eventually surfaced, minus the jewels and in the canary-yellow David Nieper number. She waved away tonight's dinner. Mildred asked that I join her in the living room, where she explained that she was too distressed to eat as she was so anxious that she'd told Maggie too much, that she'd been too raunchy. Mildred decided she'd have to call Maggie in the morning and tell her to cut out all the 'crap'.

She picked up her *Daily Express* and turned to where she'd circled tonight's viewing. She turned on the TV and settled down.

I left Mildred as she swallowed three Rennies while complaining about the poor quality of acting on *Emmerdale Farm*. She turned down the volume as she shouted to Joanna and me in the kitchen.

'Oh, this is a pile of shit,' she said, giving us a running commentary on who was onscreen. 'Oh, Gawd! I can't stand this fat female,' she yelled. 'Oh, she is just too awful!' she screamed. 'At least Flynn fancied me. God, this female wouldn't have had a chance.'

* * *

Mildred recounted her attempted rape by Errol Flynn many further times. Once, as I sat with her after midnight in the A&E department of Chelsea and Westminster Hospital, when she was convinced she was dying though really she only had heartburn, Mildred told a couple next to her who she'd been in Hollywood. As we waited and waited, Mildred talked and talked. Her stories intensified, concluding, as they usually did, with the Errol Flynn assault. A young lady sitting next to me had been listening. She whispered to me that she too had been a victim of rape. I introduced her to Mildred. They both wept.

Once, in a café with my friend Malcolm, she talked loudly about the time she had been invited to Paradise Ranch, the home of rich and powerful movie director Cecil B. DeMille. According to Mildred, she had arrived to discover DeMille stripped to the waist in plus-fours, mowing the lawn to the applause of his long-term lover, the actress Julia Faye. But dinner that night turned out to be a quiet affair – just the two of them. Julia was nowhere to be seen.

'My place setting was awash with packets of silk stockings. A fully-liveried butler then served me oysters with the pearls still attached. We drank mint juleps in frosted cut glasses which, as the ice melted, revealed the DeMille monogram.'

Wearing an ermine cape and a green satin evening gown, which he'd left for her on the bed of her room, Mildred had found herself under his intense gaze. Knowing it could become awkward, Mildred had excused herself, climbed out the window, and hitchhiked home to Allah.

Astounded by her candour, Malcolm reminded me later of the deathly silence that fell on the coffee shop that day. Such was the volume of her voice that she'd almost shouted out, 'Errol Flynn tried to rape me' as she embarked on telling Malcolm her stories. 'A woman at the next table's rum baba fell from her fork, and her friend almost poured tea into her lap,' remembered Malcolm. 'All eyes were most definitely on Mildred – they were always on Mildred.'

Eleven

The Premiere

I was in the office when Howard rang my mobile. He told me that he'd met up with his friend Dominick a couple of days ago, and that Dominick knew someone managing the guest list for the Royal Premiere of *The Aviator*, a biopic about the early life of movie mogul Howard Hughes. Impressed with his stories of Mildred, Dominick then had arranged for Howard to meet the PR people working on the film for a bite to eat at L'Escargot on Greek Street. I imagined how Howard had sold Mildred to them. A great raconteur with a memory for details like no other, he would have easily remembered the name of Clarice Sherry, the starlet Hughes had dumped in order to date Mildred. He would have teased them with Mildred's stories about how Hughes wore scruffy clothes, and where he'd taken Mildred to purchase the latest golf-clubs, and then who'd been at the Wilshire Country Club during their game: Mildred, a sure-fire hit who often shot in the seventies, versus Hughes, with his two handicap.

In possession of two tickets to the premiere, Howard was calling to say that unfortunately, due to another longstanding engagement, he wasn't able to take her the following night, so would I go in his place? I should have been ecstatic, but following her performance in the coffee shop on Primrose Hill the previous month, I wondered if I could stand another episode of The Mildred Shay Show.

Howard assured me there would be small chance of Mildred launching into a great tirade; it was a film premiere, she'd have to be quiet. I took the bait.

Mildred informed me over breakfast that morning that she'd not slept a wink, so worried was she about what to wear in the evening. At four in the morning, she had finally decided on something she'd located at the back of her closet, something she felt was suitably 'Hollywood'. We both left the flat at the same time: she in a taxi headed for Lady Davidson's hairdresser, Michelle Jones, and me for the office.

Mildred had rung Michelle on her mobile as soon as I'd delivered the news to her the previous night. I'd heard her telling Michelle all about Howard Hughes, how mean he was with his money on their first date to Santa Monica Pier, how he'd scolded her when she pushed him for a few dimes to ride the rollercoaster.

As we went our separate ways, I promised to come home from work early to help her get ready.

I got home at four to find Mildred beautifully coiffured and sitting in front of the mirror in the make-up room. Behind her, hanging off one of the old Louis Vuitton trunks, was the chosen gown. She was talking at me while applying mascara to false eyelashes, sharing further stories of Howard Hughes: how she'd been dating him when, in 1934, he'd set his first aviation record by flying at an unprecedented 185 miles per hour, and how they'd danced – she beautifully, he dreadfully – at the famed Cocoanut Grove later that night.

Some of the names Mildred mentioned I recognised; however, I was more concerned with what was staring back at me from the hanger, and wondering how best to talk her out of it and into something else.

The best way to describe the dress was 1980s wedding: a giant, shiny, Lady Diana-style meringue with indescribably wide shoulders. But the creation before me was definitely intended for a bridesmaid, with multiple layers of apricot-coloured frills and froth. Turning back to Mildred, I watched as she applied more orange panstick. I feared that, once in the dress, fellow guests would be unable to determine where her skin ended and the dress began. She'd look like an Oompa Loompa in drag.

I left Mildred concentrating on pencilling in her eyebrows. I headed to my bedroom to get ready. I was about to have a shower when she knocked on the door. She didn't wait for an answer and barged in. Usually she would make a joke about seeing me in my boxers; however, she was in too much of a state. If the dress had been long on her in the 80s, it was swamping her now.

'Do you think you could pin it up?' she asked me.

The dress had looked frightful on the hanger and now, on Mildred, it was even worse. Details I'd missed earlier now seem somehow magnified: bows on the shoulders, beads and sequins at the waist. The overall look was sickly-sweet against her dazzlingly blonde hair and carmine lipstick. The general impression was of Bette Davis dolled up as Baby Jane Hudson for a night on the town.

She opened the wardrobe door, the one with the full-length mirror on the reverse, and considered her own reflection. In her hand she was holding an orange, pink, and silver bird of paradise hat. She placed it on her head.

'I'm wondering if it's too much...' she said, her right hand on her hip.

Although I eventually managed to talk her into wearing her favourite black batwing dress, she told me that she'd happened upon the apricot gown while being fitted for her costume for her tiny 'bit part' in the film *Superman III* and had asked the costumier if she could have it. Mildred had always got a kick out of being a part of the Superman franchise, despite her role being very minor.

I remembered that early on in our flat-share Mildred had been absolutely ecstatic to see *Superman III* in the TV listings. She'd not watched it for years, and therefore circled it in red in her newspaper and made a note of timings in her diary.

Both fans of *Superman*, Joanna and I had decided to turn the TV showing into a mini-premiere. When the day – a rainy Saturday afternoon – arrived, we banished Mildred to her bedroom while I put on a tuxedo and Joanna dressed the living room. We positioned the recliner directly in front of the television screen, with a dining chair and the library chair alongside.

Joanna had decided she'd go further than just flinging on a frock. She'd always loved fancy dress. Wearing an assortment of Mildred's clothes (a tight black mini-skirt over black fishnets), Joanna was in panto mood. She looked every inch an usherette circa 1960, complete with an usherette's tray which she'd fashioned from a cardboard box picked up at Mr Ali's earlier in the week. With popcorn in colourful paper bags and penny-sweets placed in little plastic cups, we were ready to go.

We hadn't had to coax Mildred into joining in: once Joanna had mentioned the idea of a screening she had been instantly on board. I knocked on her door, and on opening it found her wearing a long black cowl-neck Lurex dress teamed with black opera gloves, a plume of ostrich feathers in her hair, and her ermine cape – the bounty she'd absconded with seventy years earlier when she fled Paradise Ranch and the raunchy Cecil B. DeMille.

Taking Joanna's arm, she had teetered precariously along the hall in strappy scandals, bowing to the glossy photographs of her film star friends on the walls as we passed. In the living room, Joanna played *She's a Star* by James on the CD player. We danced around (Mildred having kicked off her shoes almost immediately) like a trio of teenagers as the film started.

Popcorn finished, sweets eaten, vodka martinis drunk; we all sat waiting for Mildred's 'bit' alongside her beloved Geoffrey (who after his military career had started acting too) in the final elevator scene with Christopher Reeve. She'd wept throughout the film, so profound was her love for her late co-star. I knew he was on her prayer list every night.

Then, adding to her distress, another disaster: for some reason, her and Geoffrey's brief moment of glory had been cut! Mildred informed us she had every intention of ringing the network on Monday morning, determined that they should repeat the film the following Saturday with her and Geoffrey's appearances intact.

* * *

As we headed to Leicester Square for the *Aviator* premiere in the back of a chauffeur-driven car, arranged for us by a contact of Howard's, Mildred's state of excitement was invigorated still further by searchlights and the roar of the crowd.

She took my arm as we walked up the red carpet. On either side of us were screaming fans held captive behind crash barriers. Despite feeling energised, Mildred edged at a snail's pace down the red carpet. I bent down to her level to ask if she felt alright. She simply beamed her intention to be seen by as many people as possible.

Once we were shown to our seats inside the auditorium she glanced around her, asking me in loud whispers who 'the dame with the breasts might be,' and if I could tell her which programme the 'exotic fella' had been in on TV.

She didn't stop talking until a man at the front introduced the film and its stars, who were sitting three rows in front of us. I nudged Mildred as Leonardo DiCaprio rose from his seat and waved, but she was far more interested in giggling with the handsome black guy next to her. As the din died down, the last words I heard were Mildred's:

'Fella, you wouldn't happen to remember Hollywood's Pocket Venus?'

As the film began to roll, I watched Mildred instead.

Her face told me she'd been catapulted back decades by watching scenes of the old Cocoanut Grove at the Ambassador Hotel. She pulled from her pocketbook her mother's Tiffany opera glasses. But from the way they were directed, I could tell she wasn't watching the film; she was watching someone else in the audience.

'Psst! Who is that boy down there?' she asked, and handed me her opera glasses. 'You need these?'

I presumed she meant Leonardo DiCaprio but took the glasses from her anyway.

'You recognise him?' she asked.

'It's Leonardo DiCaprio,' I said, leaning into her ear.

'Oh, you don't say.' Mildred took back the glasses. 'What a minute...let me get a better look. Oh, it's the same boy as the one on the screen.'

A man in front of us leant back and tapped my knee to tell me to shut up. For a while, thankfully, Mildred was quiet.

We were about twenty-five minutes into the film when she poked me again.

'That boy, who's he playing?' she asked.

'That's Leonardo, Cissie! He's the lead, he's playing Howard Hughes.'

She sniggered. 'Oh, no! Oh, but really, darling, that's awful. Howard Hughes was a man, and he looks like a good-looking lesbian!'

The man in front, who'd previously been angry with us, turned and laughed, as did Mildred's new young friend to her left, and the woman next to him.

At the after-party, Mildred made a beeline for Leonardo, but we were warned off by one of his minders. I wondered if word had spread that the 'old blonde lady' had been a girlfriend of Hughes' and hadn't much liked his portrayal.

'Who the hell does that kid think he is?' she said as she stomped off towards the bar. 'Howard Hughes may have been a mean son-of-a-bitch, but he had manners.'

It was there, sitting on a low sofa, that I spotted Luise Rainer. Despite both living in Belgravia, they'd barely exchanged more than a polite hello since the thirties when both were under contract to Metro-Goldwyn-Mayer. Rainer, a true screen legend, the first actress ever to win back-to-back Oscars, was for all intents and purposes the guest of honour.

It was Mildred who struck up a conversation first, looking somewhat robust as she loomed over the waif-like Luise. She was dressed head-to-toe in gold, including a gold crocheted skull-cap and gold kitten heels. As they talked, it became clear Luise couldn't recall Mildred.

'Vot films did you do?' she asked, her accent still heavy Austrian.

'Oh, God, Johnny Weissmuller, William Lundigan, Glenn Ford, Howard Hughes, Victor Mature...'

Luise looked puzzled. 'I said films. Vot films did you do?' she repeated.

'Oh, shit, Luise!' Mildred roared with laughter. 'I thought you were asking what affairs I had!' She took a deep swig of champagne. 'Come on, Luise, who did you do?' she asked, winking.

Luise remained tight-lipped as she slowly stood up (with my help), bid Mildred farewell, and all but glided over to Cate Blanchett, who had played Katharine Hepburn in *The Aviator*.

'Christ!' said Mildred, polishing off her drink. 'Would you get a load of her? The Oscar-winner. Why, she even dresses like an Academy Award.'

'Well, she was a pioneer, Mildred – Luise Rainer made history,' I said. I was getting a kick out of winding her up a little.

'She's older than me by years!' she said, finishing her drink and looking for another. 'She was always so prissy! Irving Thalberg told me he found her a goddamn uptight son of a bitch.'

We spent the remainder of the night topping up our champagne and people-watching. Mildred passed comment rather loudly on everyone who walked past her, and criticised Princess Eugenie's dress as being too dowdy – that was, until her mother, the Duchess of York, took the trouble to come over to us and tell Mildred how lovely she looked. Afterwards, Mildred judged the Princess to be the epitome of elegance. Instead, she began critiquing the men in the room. Her most venomous attack was on Harvey Weinstein, purely because he was, in her words, 'so fat, and I can't stand fat.'

* * *

As the clock struck five on Sunday afternoon, I headed to the balcony for a cigarette. Mildred had called Baby. The French doors were ajar. I could hear every word: she was saying how she'd met the star of the picture.

'He's a boy-man, darling…Oh, of course I spoke with him, Baby, but he's full of himself, and besides, I was busy socialising with producers and royalty. I tell you, even the Duchess of Kent said how beautiful I looked…' Mildred changed the conversation when she spied me and instead asked after Gordon, Sun, the dogs, and even Baby's lodger.

After hanging up, Mildred accused me of 'eavesdropping' in on private conversations. I decided to pull her leg and asked at what point she'd spoken to Leonardo DiCaprio and how it was that she'd chatted with the Duchess of Kent when she hadn't been there. 'Oh, I was throwing the shit around,' she said, half-laughing, and she tossed the TV guide at me. 'It's Baby: she needs to know her Mama's okay, that I'm well. She worries about me.'

Suddenly Mildred changed the topic and started complaining that I should have negotiated an appearance fee for her. Why should she have had to drag her arse across London to talk to a bunch of newspaper men for nothing?

* * *

Avoiding neighbours was our normal practice, but as I turned onto Cundy Street, I came face to face with fellow resident Inga Schmidt and her usual grievances: the volume of Mildred's television and the shower which had started to make growling sounds like someone being violently sick. In particular, she wanted to talk about a recent problem: Inga had witnessed – or rather, her cleaner had seen whilst emptying 'Madame's' rubbish in the main refuge area – half-empty cat food tins and the contents of Rosebud's litter tray tumbling from the direction of Mildred's garbage chute.

Rant over, Inga stepped aside and let me pass so I could make my escape into the lift and get to the fourth floor. The doors opened, and there stood Mildred. She was convinced someone had tried to kidnap me. She'd read about Triad gangs. Then she'd wondered if I'd had a fall. I led her back into the flat. She wandered over to the recliner, where she'd left her scrapbooks. She had been looking at photographs of herself and Howard Hughes. She felt sure that looking down at her books for the past hour had caused something to go wrong with her neck. I calmed her by massaging her shoulders. It was then that she asked me about my conversation with Inga, which I reluctantly described.

She spent the next two days with the television on top volume and the shower running even when unoc-cupied. She tossed Rosebud's soiled cat litter directly down the rubbish chute. After all, Mildred had been throwing shit around her whole life.

Then, worried Inga would 'dob her in to the Duke', the remainder of that week was spent languishing in her recliner, refusing food and dressed in little except her collection of David Nieper nighties.

It was only when Howard called to see if Mildred would like to accompany him to a cocktail party at The Groucho one evening that her mood changed. She slunk into the make-up room and set about working on her face.

She and Howard found me in the living room when they returned from the party. Joanna was already in bed.

Howard had introduced Mildred to Tracey Emin. Mildred was very vocal about Emin's unmade bed. I tried to put an end to her jibes by telling Mildred she could better the 'unmade bed' with her 'untidy flat'. She had no idea what I was talking about, even though she had stepped over a pile of Rosebud's faeces that morning.

Instead, pissed, she stood and beamed at us both. 'God, darling, Princess Diana had her 'rock', but you know what? You two are my bricks.' She giggled. 'That's bricks, darling, not pricks!'

* * *

The following Friday morning, Joanna and I were home alone and in bed. Mildred had been collected by a hospital worker to be taken in for a check-up.

Joanna snuggled into me as we lay in bed together. We had both been so busy with work, and so dominated by Mildred, that we had only used the bed to sleep in what felt like weeks.

Our long doze was interrupted by the phone. I jumped from our bed to answer it. The voice was unmistakably Mildred. She was ready for collection and wouldn't take hospital transport. She'd wait outside the hospital for me. Joanna suggested that in the absurdly glamorous get-up she'd chosen for the hospital she need not worry; she'd soon get picked up.

As I dressed, I reflected on our lives now. There was nobody else. I knew Joanna was unhappy. Already she was planning to go; would I be the next to fall?

Twelve

Tai chi

*J*oanna had started her new job in Gloucestershire. She and I had had a row about my job prospects in the Forest of Dean, so, in protest, I'd decided to stay in London for the weekend. But by eleven on Saturday morning, I wished I'd gone anyway, or perhaps paid my parents a visit in Sussex. I'd had enough of Mildred's tipsiness and her continuous jibes about why Joanna had decided to leave me. She teased me as we were watching *Saturday Kitchen* by saying Joanna had probably found herself a 'farm-boy' like the hapless 'Dingle' chump on *Emmerdale Farm*. She was sure Joanna had a new 'type' and would be chasing brawn not brains these days. I left the room. Mildred called after me.

'Orstin, if I were you I'd just let her go!'

I went to Starbucks in Orange Square. Mildred called three times; I let each one go to answerphone. I toyed with the idea of ringing Joanna, but I knew she'd just tell me to leave for good. We kept fighting over what I would do in the Forest of Dean if we moved there, as Joanna wanted to. Joanna had suggested I could return to hospitality, having once managed a restaurant in Wimbledon Village. She felt there would be plenty of opportunities at local hotels and pubs. But despite everything, I wasn't done with London yet. And whenever we argued, it was Joanna who brought up Mildred's health and fragility. She would have pangs of guilt. She knew that I couldn't leave because there was simply nobody else to care for her. So the situation stayed as it was: Joanna and I as long-distance lovers.

* * *

By the end of the week Mildred had declared herself an invalid. Her right eye wouldn't stop watering. She'd taken drops and painkillers, and made an appointment to see her GP. I suspected that this condition had developed because she was annoyed that I, being distracted by the fight with Joanna, was not paying her enough attention.

Nevertheless she asked that I accompany her to St Mary's for the Sunday ten o'clock service. She felt guilty about demanding appearance fees and being 'horrid' earlier in the week to Joanna for not calling me enough (even though I had explained she called my mobile, not the house phone). Therefore Mildred needed to ask forgiveness from the Almighty. Mildred told me she'd been up half the night with worry.

She was already fully made-up when I rose at eight. Yet despite this, Mildred took so long to get dressed that I feared we would have to all but run to the church to make it in time. Part of the reason for the delay was a further discovery of moths. She noticed a giant hole in the sleeve of a favourite cardigan - the one, she told me, that she was sure had belonged to the King.

'Mildred, I didn't know you'd been in the practice of borrowing clothes from Elvis Presley!' I joked, knowing full well she meant George VI. Looking at it, I doubted the cardie, a dismal orange-ish colour, would have come from either Elvis' or King George's wardrobe. I told her so. Mildred held the item up to the light and decided it was a more recent acquisition – it must have belonged to Frank Sinatra.

Since she was refusing to yield to 'the bugs', I helped her conceal the damage with a fragment of material from an old blouse that she'd squirrelled away in a drawer – along with buttons, trimmings, and old knicker elastic during the Big Clean. Finally out of the door, we speed-walked towards Bourne Street and St Mary's.

As we turned down Elizabeth Street from Ebury Street, Mildred noticed Lady Colin Campbell coming in our direction. We stopped and chatted, Mildred having met her a few times at the presbytery after Sunday service.

'Well, Mildred, you always knew how to get a man, dear!' said Lady Colin as she nodded to me.

Mildred did her best Mae West impression and retorted, 'Ooh, but this one is so old! He's twenty-something. I need a younger model to come up and see me sometime.'

Listening to her chat with Lady Colin, I discovered why Mildred had been determined to get to church today. Her talk about wanting forgiveness for saying mean things to Joanna was probably nonsense. Lady Colin confirmed there was a new priest, Father Cherry, at St Mary's. Mildred had spoken with the newbie on the telephone a few days before and was determined that she'd be one of the first female parishioners to meet him. Lady Colin's sustained conversation put an end to that goal. By the time we arrived, actresses Cicely Paget-Bowman and Sue Lloyd had 'taken her Cherry', as Mildred put it furiously.

The next morning I'd received two missed phone calls by the time I reached the office. I'd told Mildred many times that Mondays were usually busy on the paper. My boss allowed me out of a meeting with him and three others to take her fifth call of the morning – it was just after ten.

The landline was engaged when I tried to call her back. A moment later, Mildred was ringing me. She said she'd felt unwell the previous day, but had decided to keep it to herself so as not to worry me. I remarked that she had seemed perfectly well gossiping with her friends at church. She insisted she'd actually been masking how ill she had been feeling for a while now. She told me she had not wanted to add to my distress at being dumped by my betrothed. Then she had to ring off. She was waiting for a doctor to make a house call and she'd only pencilled in one eyebrow and wasn't wearing lipstick yet.

I called Mildred again during my lunch break. She was elated. Dr Thomas had prescribed her a five-day course of antibiotics. I wondered what was wrong, as she seemed fine to me. Mildred asked me to try and leave work early because someone needed to pick up the prescription. As I didn't get back to the flat until six, the local chemist was closed. An hour later, having caught the bus, I was waiting in the 24-hour chemist on Hyde Park Corner.

I returned with the medicine. Mildred was eager to start the course. She asked that I sit on her bed and join her in prayer. She had added Suzanne Kaaren to the long list of individuals she gave extra thought to in times of prayer. Below Suzanne, she had pencilled in my name. I asked her why the sudden attention. I discovered, as she flicked through her tiny notes, that my name was written in her spidery hand over and over and over, like one would write lines as punishment from a school teacher.

'Family,' she mouthed.

The following evening, I was out at the John Snow pub on Broadwick Street with my friend Barry and his colleagues, Lee, Nick, and Ben, all graphic designers at Turner Classic Movies. I found myself talking about Mildred more than about Joanna, who'd called me on the way to the pub. She was annoyed – jealous, I would have wagered – that I was out in London and she was stuck in the Forest of Dean. Lee joked that Joanna was jealous that I'd got myself a new woman – albeit an older model, a very old model. 'She'd predate the Model T Ford!' he goaded.

I checked my phone on the way back from the gents'. Joanna had left a message to say she hoped I had a good evening and to pass her best on to the boys. Mildred had left four messages, each one more anxious than the last; she'd forgotten I was out tonight. Nick appeared behind me. Mildred's voice message was so loud that he heard every word. 'Your new bird checking up on you?' he joked.

I pretended not to care and shoved the phone back in my pocket, then headed to the bar to buy another round. While waiting for the barman, I mulled over what would happen next. I'd received an increase in wages, and Joanna was earning good money now too, but I couldn't bear to tell Mildred I wanted to leave. I ordered a whiskey and downed it before I returned to the boys with a fresh round of pints.

By closing time, I was well and truly pissed. I caught the 38 bus back to the flat. It was nearly midnight by the time I'd negotiated my way in a snake-like fashion down Ebury Street.

I woke up the next morning feeling sick and immediately dashed to the toilet. I was still wearing some of my clothes from the previous night. The room span as I returned to bed. I detected movement outside my bedroom. Shakily, I got up to open the door. It was Mildred.

'Oh, you are here. I was worried. I went to bed after eleven and, because you hadn't called, I got thinking you'd been murdered by the Triads, or worse, had left me for some other broad.' She had in her hand one of my shoes, one sock, and a V-neck jumper. 'These were on my recliner. What were you doing last night?' she asked. 'A striptease?'

I reminded her I had been meeting Barry and his work colleagues, and confessed that I'd drunk a lot. She wasn't registering what I was telling her. She sat on my bed. I advised her not to come too close. She laughed at my feeble state and then turned more serious.

'Listen, I'm here on a mission. Prince Rainier has

died.' She made the sign of the cross. 'I thought I should wake you in case you can write his obituary for the paper.' She left my room. 'Just don't mention me in it.'

I drank an entire pot of black coffee as well as Mildred's hangover cure: a 'Prairie Oyster', as she called it. Mildred brought it to me as I was getting dressed and stood, hands on hips, until I'd swallowed it all: raw egg, tomato juice, vinegar, and something tangy. Mildred told me she was a dab hand: she'd made many a Prairie Oyster for all three of her husbands – for the first and second more often than for Geoffrey.

Mildred left me creeping around the flat. She had an appointment at four with the new dentist who'd taken over at the local Belgravia practice. She was anxious at the thought of having someone new 'playing' with her expensive Beverley Hills bridge.

The flat was eerily quiet when I got home that evening. I called out 'hello'. Nothing. Still feeling ropey from the night before, I almost vomited from the shock of finding Mildred, not in the make-up room, nor her bedroom, nor horizontal in the recliner, but on the floor behind the dining table. I dropped my bag as I surged towards her. For a moment I just stood over her and feared that this was the end. I wondered if she had suffered a stroke. I knelt down and placed my hand on her shoulder.

'Christ! You scared me,' she screamed. I yelled in shock. She pointed to her hearing aids on the mantelpiece. 'Pass me those. Fuck, you could've given me a heart attack,' she scolded me as she 'tuned in'.

I helped Mildred to her feet. She made the sign of

the cross when I told her I had thought she was dead. Sitting in the recliner, she told me that her new dentist was a darling 'Chinaman' and a practitioner of tai chi. As luck would have it, Mildred had been Dr Kim's last patient of the day and he'd taken 'a healthy interest' in her.

Up on her feet, she held onto the standard lamp to demonstrate how she'd lifted her leg high up onto Dr Kim's desk. Then, moving about the living room, she illustrated some of the basic tai chi moves he'd shown her. Ten minutes later, she had me on the carpet. After twenty minutes I was feeling rather relieved that this new hobby was a silent practice – my head was *still* spinning.

Cross-legged in the middle of the living room, dressed in her Jane Fonda-esque leotard, Mildred whispered how she had not felt such peace since she and Geoffrey had taken themselves off to a religious retreat in Joshua Tree, high in the Californian desert, during the 1960s. 'I remained in silent meditation for days,' she exclaimed.

I could hardly imagine it – Mildred talked even in her sleep.

It was Rosebud who put an end to the new tai-chi routine. Perhaps unnerved by the prolonged tranquillity, on the evening of day six of the new fad she lashed out at Mildred while she was sprawled on the living room floor. On the second pounce, Rosebud's claw became entangled in Mildred's cardigan.

'Oh, Rosie! What are you doing?' she yelled, upset that the cat had torn Sinatra's cardigan.

Rosebud then went in for the kill: she gave a scratch to Mildred's face and put another on her neck. Before I could free Mildred, Rosebud had sliced a chunk from her thumb, which left her victim pouring blood. Satisfied, the attacker disappeared.

While helping Mildred to her feet, I noticed the cut was quite deep. I cleaned, disinfected, and bandaged it.

The next morning, I found Mildred in the recliner. She couldn't locate Rosebud. She was sorry, she was sad, she had promised Rosie she'd ditch tai chi and go back to the Bible. So grieved was Mildred that she hadn't noticed her hand had swollen to twice its usual size. I left her with Dermot Murnaghan while I rang her GP surgery. The receptionist suggested a tetanus vaccine booster.

After Mildred had selected an outfit and completed her make-up, we were ready to go for a trip to the surgery. I left her in the waiting room after fifteen minutes of chatting 'bunions and Rivers of Blood' with Lady Enoch Powell.

Thirteen

Medication

I received a call on my mobile at work, swiftly followed by four more when I didn't answer immediately. It was eleven when Marina, who sat next to me in the office, snapped that I should just pick it up.

Mildred said she felt terrible. She blamed me for sending her blood pressure through the roof and prompting today's dizzy spells and chest pains. I asked what she'd taken for them. Her answer: a vodka martini to combat the stress. I urged her to call her surgery.

'Darling, do you think I haven't done that? But that female bitch on the desk hasn't called me back, so I've been trying to call her. I'm an old woman, for Christ's sake.'

By twelve-thirty, Marina had agreed to cover for me when our boss returned from his lunch meeting. I left in a hurry. It was only May and yet it was sizzling in the city – I was left hot and sticky from dashing across London to 'rescue' her.

When I arrived, Mildred was on the phone to her surgery again, saying she felt terrible. When she saw me, she hung up. The doctor had suggested she take herself to the Casualty department at Chelsea & Westminster. She'd rung for an ambulance.

'Will you come with me?' she asked. 'I don't think I can face this one alone.'

I found out later that, being cross that I'd ignored her calls, she'd initially phoned others before having to surrender and ask me. She had tried her priest – away; her old friend Cicely – no answer; Lady Janet – unwell; and finally Tyrone at Argos. He'd left the store and the 'female' Mildred had spoken to had refused to pass on his details.

Imagining the ambulance with its flashing blue lights tearing down the King's Road and clipping the edge of Sloane Square at top speed, I tried to get Mildred ready as quickly as possible.

She said she couldn't possibly be taken to hospital in what she was currently wearing: a pale pink leisure suit. Mildred stood at the bank of wardrobes, deciding what to wear. She pulled out the Pucci dress, but deemed it too much. She'd forgotten about the Norman Hartnell 'Le Petit Salon' turquoise suit with cream piping – lost for perhaps years in the depths of her wardrobe, hidden under three other items of clothing on a single hanger. However, this too was rejected as, after trying on the jacket, she worried it might get 'infested' at the hospital by the 'super-bugs' she'd read about in her *Daily Express*. Next, she picked out the Greek number.

'Hmm...a bit too continental...They'll think I'm some kinda tourist,' she concluded once she'd taken a closer inspection. I was furious by now. I pulled out a pair of grey cotton flares and a canary-yellow fitted top. I tossed both onto her bed and headed for the kitchen to cool off.

'And I'll need a jacket,' she called, even though it was sweltering outside. She passed me on her way to the make-up room to prep her face. I spied the brown Hardy Amies jacket on the chair beside the dressing-table and handed it to her.

'I'll need a scarf too, dahling, otherwise the outfit looks too plain,' she said.

With half an eyebrow painted on, she walked past me and returned to her bedroom. I followed, trying to hurry her along. She tugged silk scarves from the tired pink chest of drawers close to her bed. She wouldn't be rushed. I left her once more and went to the loo.

'Oh, Orstin, I need you,' she yelled. I found her holding a large square scarf in her hands. 'Did I ever show you this? I picked this up on one of our trips to Europe on the *Île de France*. Isn't it gorgeous?'

The ship itself, in all its faded art deco glory, was the centrepiece of the design.

'We always took a first-class cabin. Daddy only wanted the best for his girls. Did I ever tell you that we met Josephine Baker on one of these trips?'

'It's wonderful, Mildred,' I said, not letting her give the anecdote. 'Now, we must finish getting you ready.'

Resting on her bed, Mildred launched into a story about having been on board the *Queen Mary*. Apparently, on this particular voyage, everyone on board fell ill besides Mildred, Marlene Dietrich, and Noël Coward. I pulled her to her feet as I assisted her with tying the scarf around her shoulders. She was in the past, reliving the experience: playing Murder in the Dark with her famous friends. To make the game more exciting they included a cabin boy, Marlene's maid, and a handsome young American man who, she recalled, was Rose Kennedy's gym instructor.

'Imagine it; practically everyone was sick aside from me.' As I helped her pin a large brooch to the lapel of the jacket, I found it hard to imagine that she, of all people, hadn't felt sick.

'I can't believe that Cissie,' I said, finally managing the clasp. 'You didn't have even a minor twinge?'

We were interrupted by loud a knock at the front door. The ambulance men hadn't needed to buzz the intercom. I later discovered that the Duke of Kent had let them in. I met the Duke some time later and he mentioned 'the Hollywood personality who lives in the building who rather likes to make a fuss'.

I rushed to answer the door.

'You got a 999 here?' a tall blond guy asked, looking about the hall. At that, Mildred appeared. She shimmied along the hallway as if it were a catwalk.

'Well, hello, boys,' she said seductively.

'Can you walk? Or do we need to strap you in the chair?' the shorter one of the two asked curtly.

'Wait a cotton-pickin' minute, honey, I'm not ready yet,' she replied abruptly, annoyed that her alluring tone had fallen on deaf ears. She placed the Hardy Amies jacket around her shoulders and reluctantly sat in the chair.

'You don't have to strap me in,' she said to the shorter man. 'I'm off to Chelsea and Westminster, kiddo, not Guantanamo Bay!'

As we waited for the lift, Mildred shouted, 'Oh,

Orstin, my sunglasses!' The two men patiently held the lift as I ran back in and grabbed them from the small table next to her recliner.

Once we were outside, the back doors of the ambulance flew open. A young blonde girl smiled from inside as the shorter of the two men, whom she called Adam, lifted the chair in.

'Hello, there,' said the girl to Mildred. 'I think we've met before. A few times…'

* * *

Mildred had been in a cubicle in A&E for forty-five minutes. I was sitting with her. A young Indian doctor had done various tests and we were waiting for the results.

'Oh, Doctor, should we wait here or shall we go to the lounge?'

'I think you mean the waiting room? Just stay here for a bit longer if you can. It shouldn't be much longer.'

As he stepped back from behind the curtain, Mildred nodded her head to where he was standing.

'He's a dark handsome type. A bit young maybe, but when he matures he'll be a dead ringer for that newsreader George Alagiah.'

I took no notice, frustrated that I had left the office yet again to join Mildred back on her favourite stage: A&E at Chelsea and Westminster.

As it turned out, just as it had been over Christmas at the Dilke, the chest pains were simply indigestion. The doctor asked her about her diet.

'Well, my boyfriend here likes to feed me and is trying to make me fat.'

She slapped my knee to add to her comic routine.

'I've read about these couples who get their rocks off by over-feeding their partners. They call them 'feeders',' she laughed. 'Maybe that's a kink I have yet to discover – much to the detriment of my waistline.'

The doctor gave an awkward smile.

'Have you heard of the Pocket Venus?' she said.

'No, but I've certainly heard of you,' he said shortly.

We waited for the ambulance to arrive to take her back to the apartment. I said she could take a taxi, but Mildred was insistent. 'Orstin, the neighbours saw us leave in an ambulance with the lights flashing. I can hardly just mosey on back there now in a black cab as if nothing has happened.'

I was lost for words. I hailed a cab for myself and headed back to the office.

Back at the flat that night, the phone rang. It was Lady Janet. 'Oh, hello, dahling.' Mildred paused. 'Yeah. It was pretty heavy stuff. I think the doctor said there might be something wrong with my intestines.'

I heard Lady Janet ask another question. 'It could be my kidneys?' repeated Mildred quizzically. 'Oh, Orstin. Lady Janet thinks it could be my kidneys. You think I should call the surgery?'

I didn't bother to answer. I stayed late at the office the next day, and after work I met Kirsty for a quick drink near Victoria Station. As I finished my second Guinness, and she her second white wine, Kirsty urged me to consider a change of atmosphere.

The next day, Mildred felt too unwell to eat. She'd been reading about energy drinks and suggested I add a few to the shopping basket next time I was at Sainsbury's.

That evening, despite claiming she couldn't touch a thing, she appeared next to me in the kitchen whilst I was making myself a late snack of salmon stir-fry. 'It smells gorgeous. Maybe I should just have *un petit morceau*.'

Hearing that, I split my dish in two and served her a plate, complete with vegetables and noodles. She took the tray from me and polished off the lot.

I was woken that night by the sound of the television. It was almost midnight. I woke Mildred in the recliner and urged her to go to bed. 'Gosh. I am exhausted, darling.' Then she stopped.

'Oh, Orstin. I have a sore right tit. Do you think I have something?'

I replied tersely, 'It's late,' and returned to my bedroom. She called after me to ask whether she should perhaps call for an ambulance. I slammed my bedroom door.

* * *

I heard Mildred. I looked at my alarm clock: six-thirty. I found her pacing up and down in the living room, Rosebud stalking close behind her. She'd had a terrible night's sleep, scared that maybe the doctor was wrong and it was more than gas. 'Lady Janet knows this stuff. She wouldn't have mentioned kidneys if she didn't.' She peered down the top of her *Care Bears* nightdress. 'Perhaps it's breast cancer?'

I made builder's tea and toast for me and yoghurt with muesli and a Lady Grey tea for her. I carried her breakfast into the living room – where she was topless and massaging her right breast. I placed her tray on a side table. She hardly noticed me.

I called out to her from the hall thirty minutes later, 'Bye, Cissie. See you tonight.' Only it wasn't that night. Nor was it the afternoon. I was back at the flat within two hours. A specialist from Chelsea and Westminster had called to say they were unhappy with her blood test and were sending an ambulance.

'You had better come quickly if you still want to see me alive,' was the last message I'd picked up on my phone before dashing to take a cab. Fortunately, my boss was away. Greg and Marina in the office said they would hold the fort while I was gone. I couldn't say exactly how long I would be.

Mildred was waiting in the hall, fully dressed in the same clothes she'd worn the previous day, when I opened the door. 'Christ. I thought they'd be here by now. Do you think I should call 999 again?'

'How many times have you called them already?' I asked.

She'd called four times. I suggested she lie down in her recliner, take deep breaths and rest as we waited for the ambulance. I took my own advice and hid in my bedroom, texting Joanna to let her know the latest, and Howard, as I hoped he'd be able to relieve me at some point so I could get back to work.

Mildred sat for what seemed like only seconds. Then I could hear her scurrying about in her bedroom. Moments later she was standing in my doorway wearing a thin pink sweater. In her hand she was holding a wide mink scarf. Mildred was sure nobody at the hospital would have seen such expensive fur before.

There was a bang on the front door.

I jumped up and opened it to find one of the two guys from the ambulance crew yesterday, joined this time by a female companion. Mildred was right behind me, holding her handbag.

'Hello again, Miss Glamour-Puss,' the paramedic smiled. 'Back for an encore, then?'

'Yeah. Just call me Salomé!' Mildred said.

'We gonna get you in the chair or do you wanna walk this time?' he asked.

'I better take the chair in case I have a dizzy spell.' I closed the door behind her as she was manoeuvred towards the lift.

'Oh, Orstin,' she cried, her voice panicked. 'Can you fetch my Panama hat? It's hot out there and all I need now is to get a bunch of skin cancer on top of everything else.'

I opened the door and fetched the hat. Off we go again.

Back in A&E we sat and waited to be called. Mildred was looking at me. She'd only just noticed, despite claiming she had 20-20 vision, that I had been growing a beard. She didn't like it. Nor was she crazy about my casual footwear. Baby's erstwhile boyfriend Keith Moon had only ever worn sneakers.

I left her midway through her critique and walked away from her. She continued talking loudly across the room. 'I hope we don't get the Indian guy again. I think I was wrong about him. I'm not even sure if he is qualified.'

My fury must have become visible because she stopped and for a moment was quiet. 'Orstin, I know you're mad with me, but I'm gonna be a hundred soon and one hears this stuff all the time: old people left on trolleys at the mercy of interlopers like that fella – pretending to be something he's not.'

'That's ridiculous, Mildred. He might have just missed something from the scan.'

'Yeah. Like they have with Joanna's grandmother – a motherfucking tumour!'

A woman with her two young children looked over at me and tutted. I whispered an apology. I was happy when Mildred was collected by a tall bearded male nurse with three gold studs in one ear and four in the other. He assured me he'd be fine with 'Grandma', so I stayed in the waiting room, savouring the quiet.

I flicked through hand-outs offering guidance for carers. The title of one of them was *Don't Suffer in Silence*. I was so frustrated I could have cried.

When she had been gone for almost an hour, I decided to step outside into the sunshine and phone Joanna. It was nearing lunchtime, so I hoped she would be able to pick up my call. It went to voicemail. I smoked a cigarette, and as I did so I watched the doors of an ambulance open. Inside was an ancient old lady, wizened by age, holding a sad-looking teddy bear. I wondered if she had anyone with her – or if she was all alone in the world with no one to rely on, as Mildred relied on Joanna and me – now just me.

'Hello,' said the nurse with the earrings as I came back into the waiting room. 'My name is Steve, by the way.'

'Yes, sorry. I just nipped out to try and phone my fiancée.'

'That's fine, sweetie. Now, we have your Grandma. Oh, my God! She's a one, isn't she? Them stories!' he squealed. 'God, I wish I'd have been alone with them big stars from the old days.'

I nodded. 'She certainly knew a lot of famous people.'

Steve patted my hand. 'Your Nana has gallstones. Now, not to worry, hon. It'll be fine. They want to keep her in and will operate tomorrow. Well…operate. Just a tiny procedure, really. You want to go and see her?'

I was lost for words. For once, the Boy Who Cried Wolf had been right.

I found her in a cubicle. 'Oh, darling. Thank God. Oh, now, this is heavy, heavy stuff. What is the time? I need you to call Baby. Tell her that her Mama is sick and needs an emergency operation.' She hardly waited to catch her breath. 'Now, break it to her real slow that this could be the end of her Mama,' she wailed. 'The shock might do something to her. Oh, my God, my poor Baby, my poor Baby-girl. All she needs now in her life is a sick Mama.'

I checked my watch. One-thirty. Baby wouldn't yet be up for hours.

'I'll need you to go back to the flat and collect some stuff for me. Maybe just a couple of the nightgowns; nothing frilly, just some simple stuff I can keep in my locker.'

I could see her mind ticking over. 'I can get some fresh meds…I have enough in my pocketbook for now…I'll need my make-up…' She had her head in her handbag. 'Oh, good, I have my dark glasses on me.'

I scribbled a quick list as Steve came back to take Mildred to the ward. 'Come on then, Miss Superstar, we're gonna take you up to your suite now.'

Before he disappeared, I asked Steve if it was okay if I came back later. I was worried that my boss would be really pissed off with me if I continued to skip work. Steve assured me he'd look after her. I heard him tell her that 'Handsome' would be back to see her that night. I was sure she hadn't registered that, as all I heard her saying was that she'd once lived in the penthouse suite of the Regent Beverley Wilshire.

I decided to go to the flat first. I packed a bag with her requirements and put in a couple of thin sweaters and the odd scarf too, just in case. I squeezed the blue dressing gown we had bought her at Christmas into the small wheelie-case. Rosebud was crying.

'It's just you and me for the next few days,' I warned her. I headed back to the office with the case.

I had been trying to call Joanna for the past three hours; I finally got through. She had been so worried when she'd got my text message explaining everything that she had been about to get in the car and drive to London to be with me. I told her everything was in hand. She promised to drive down the next night – Friday.

When I got back to the hospital it was just after seven in the evening. The meal trolley was making its rounds, collecting dishes and leftovers from dinner. I unpacked the small case and left her to it.

'See you tomorrow then, Cissie,' I called.

'Yeah. And it's Friday the thirteenth. I need that like a hole in the head.'

I left the next morning at eight. I'd been trying to find Rosebud for the past half hour. Her food bowl was nearly empty, so I guessed she was still in the apartment and hadn't decided to make her escape whilst her 'Mama' was away.

'Oh, there you are, darling,' said Mildred when I arrived. She was sitting in the chair next to her bed. 'I'm waiting to be washed. Can you believe it? I told this large black female that I was quite capable of washing my own private parts, but she insisted. Now she has vanished, probably gone to find someone else to scrub down and fondle.'

She started to do an impression of Hattie McDaniel from *Gone with the Wind*.

I argued that she was only doing her job. 'Well, you tell her if you see her that she can do her job on someone else, for Christ's sake!'

I tried to change the subject, but she asked, 'How's my pussy? Not that one,' she added, pointing to her lap. 'Rosie.'

I failed to match her innuendo. 'I couldn't find her this morning. I thought she had joined the Foreign Legion for cats.'

Mildred couldn't see the funny side. 'Oh, no. My

God! I just don't need this stress right now.' Then, pausing, she asked, 'Orstin! You didn't leave the balcony door open overnight, did you? My God, say that man with the cholesterol' – she meant kestrel – 'decided to go for a midnight flight and the bird's gone off with my baby?'

'I doubt that, Mildred. Maybe she was enjoying some quiet time?'

Her focus switched to Baby. Had I called? What did Baby say? Did Baby ask after her? Was Gordon worried?

Baby had told me that her friend 'crazy' Carole's mother had had a gall stone procedure some weeks back, was in and out of Cedars-Sinai within twenty-four hours, and was back at the farmer's market selling produce the next day.

Mildred was angry that Baby wasn't more troubled. I reminded Mildred that she'd actually asked me not to worry Baby and that the procedure wouldn't call for more than a simple laser to remove the gallstones.

'And who told you that?' she snapped back. 'Don't tell me, that Indian doctor who told me I had gas, that I could go home and think nothing of it. Fuck. The guy doesn't know his ass from his elbow. I should phone the authorities and have him struck off for malpractice.'

I told her that it really wasn't a life and death situation, but Mildred was on the rampage. She was going to call her Canadian lawyer friend Bob Bridges at church, or the Shermans – another lawyer friend and his wife. Her outburst was cut short by the reappearance of the nurse.

'Oh, crap. It's you.'

The nurse smiled patiently. 'Yes, it's me.'

'Well, if you must get your kicks from washing old broads, then we had better go.' Mildred got up from her chair.

'Orstin, I'll catch you later – that is, if you still care enough to come and see me for – now, what was it? Oh, yeah. A 'procedure'. Fuck!'

I was in two minds about whether to go back at all. I took the bus and made my way to my office. Marina asked after Mildred.

'She's fine,' I said, 'or she will be. She's in hospital for a gallstone procedure.'

'She's lucky she has you,' Marina smiled. 'My neighbour has no one. Her husband died and they had no children.' I thought back to the old lady in the back of the ambulance with the teddy bear.

* * *

I left the office at quarter past five. Back at the hospital, I discovered Mildred wasn't in the Adele Dixon ward; she wasn't in the Francis Barnett ward either. My heart skipped a beat. It turned out Mildred had been taken down for an X-ray in preparation for her procedure.

I went for a coffee and returned an hour later. I found Mildred in a wheelchair, sitting next to her bed. For once, she had no make-up on. She was wearing the blue dressing gown, under which was a thin hospital nightdress. 'Oh, God. Don't look at me. I am a mess.'

I stared at her when she wasn't looking. She looked tiny and frail, almost bird-like. 'You see that man over there?' she said, pointing. 'Well, he told me he was waiting for his Thai wife to come and meet him. Turns out his ex-wife was Chinese – he obviously has an eye for the exotic.'

'So you've made some friends then?' She didn't answer my question.

'And Orstin, you see the poor soul over there?' I followed her finger as she pointed. 'He was injured in a car accident two years ago and still hasn't fully recovered. Isn't that terrible?'

I nodded.

'I mean, he's handsome, too.' Like that had anything to do with the tragedy of his accident; but for Mildred, looks were paramount. 'I wonder if he'll be able to get it up anymore?'

We sat together in silence for a while. I brought Mildred the newspaper to read. Every once in a while, she removed her glasses to make a comment. She had been reading a piece about violence in prisons. 'Hell. They have some female commenting here,' she said, pointing to the page. 'What do females want to work in prisons for, for God's sake? Unless they can't get any action outside so they have to go inside for a quick hard screw?'

A doctor approached us.

'Hello, Doctor. Excuse me for not getting up.'

'I am afraid we have to cancel the operation for today. The surgeon has been called away on an emergency,' he said, crouching to be at her eye level.

Mildred's tone changed. 'Well, Doctor, if this isn't an emergency then what is it? This operation I'm having is no walk in the park...'

The doctor nodded. 'I can understand your frustration, but rest assured, the procedure will go ahead as planned; just not tonight.' And with that, he got to his feet. 'So you can enjoy dinner.'

"Dinner' and 'enjoy' aren't two words I would put together, Doctor,' she said, but he was already walking away.

'Get a load of that! Christ, I've been on a knife's edge with worry all day, and some guy in a white coat just walks over and cancels the whole darn thing. Baby isn't going to like this. She's gonna be sick with worry and end up in the hospital herself.'

I left her on the ward with a beef stew followed by a sponge with custard. 'You sure I can't tempt you, darling?' she said as I grabbed my bag to leave.

'You're fine as you are.'

I told her Joanna was coming up to spend the weekend.

'Good. So you can come up and see me tomorrow before I go under. Now, you kids don't start fucking around the flat – you'll scare Rosie.'

I promised. 'Now, call Baby and break it to her gently; it's all I need for her to break under the pressure of this deadly operation and have Gordon get stressed and start drinking again. I am her life, darling,' Mildred said, dabbing the corners of her eyes with a tissue for effect.

I gave her a kiss on the cheek and turned to leave – just as Joanna walked in. She had our friend Adam with her. 'Oh, look what just swept in looking all handsome,' Mildred said, smiling. 'Isn't he a doll for showing up to see me?'

'Oh, don't be happy to see me, Cissie,' said Joanna jokingly.

'Hello, Miss Schoolmarm,' said Mildred, uninterested, before focusing on Adam. 'Now, Adam, dahling, give a dying woman a kiss, won't you?' Mildred turned to me. 'Watch her, Orstin – gay or not, she might try her luck with Mr Gorgeous here, just as I tried mine with Rudolf Nureyev. Only I,' she said, licking her index finger and wiping her eyebrow for good effect, 'won him over.'

Joanna had been to the flat, and on her way back to the car with Adam she had met Mildred's priest. On hearing that, Mildred suddenly took an interest in Joanna and asked that she ring him as soon as she was able to, and request that he add Mildred to the prayer list. I heard Mildred tell Adam that Baby was inconsolable with worry.

'Goodness, Cissie, have you spoken to Baby?' I asked her. Mildred shouted me down by saying she didn't need to actually speak with her own flesh and blood to detect when her child's heart was all but broken with anguish. Joanna grabbed my hand and mouthed for me to be quiet. She'd clearly regained some compassion through distance.

For a moment Mildred sat with her eyes shut, praying. When she opened them the same black nurse from yesterday was standing before her. Mildred introduced her to Adam and Joanna as 'the female who likes to wash older women'.

The nurse didn't react. I hated it when Mildred made such snide remarks.

'Hello, ma'am. I was wondering if you would like some tea or coffee.'

Mildred put on her best phoney upper-class accent. 'Thank-you, dear lady, but I am waiting to go down for a serious operation.'

The nurse smiled and walked away as Joanna thanked her.

Ten minutes later, an orderly of about fifty with a mass of grey curls arrived with a wheelchair. 'I have the limo, love. You ready to take a spin?'

Adam jumped up to take her arm. 'Aren't you the lucky one, with all the handsome men?' the orderly beamed.

'Yeah, and whilst this handsome one's girlfriend was in the Forest of Dean with the countryfolk I've had him all to myself,' she said, grinning at Joanna.

Mildred's illness had not taken away her ability to irritate Joanna. Adam couldn't help but give a big hearty laugh. He bade Mildred, Joanna and me farewell and headed home.

That night, back at the apartment, I cooked Joanna and I dinner; it seemed an age since it had been just the two of us alone in London. I lit the silver candlesticks I'd polished a week earlier and waited at table for Joanna, enjoying our evening together as we got slightly drunk on two bottles of Chilean Merlot. There was no denying that it had once been a beautiful apartment. Later in the evening, we made plans together: a future, a dream one day to have a small place of our own in London. Neither of us said Belgravia. That was only a pipe dream.

That night in bed Joanna drifted off to sleep in my

arms. Every now and then she jumped in her sleep; her head butted against my chin. I didn't mind. It was good to have her back again.

* * *

We arrived back at the hospital on Sunday at eleven. Mildred had already had one visitor pop by on his way to church.

The procedure had been a success; she would be out later that afternoon. I was happy, relieved that Mildred was okay. She'd spent an hour on her make-up, according to the black nurse. But part of me wanted just one more night alone with Joanna – not that that was possible anyway; she was driving back to Gloucestershire later. Part of me wanted to go with her.

After an hour, we decided to head out for a coffee and promised Mildred we would be back with a doughnut for her. We found a small café and sat enjoying the late spring sunshine, drinking coffee until it was time to head back.

As it turned out, while we had been out Mildred had suffered one of her dizzy spells. As a result, she had been ordered to remain in the hospital for tests. Quietly I was relieved.

The following morning at quarter past eight I got a call on my mobile: 'Darling, send the wagons. I am ready to come home.'

I took a quick shower and headed over to the hospital. She was sitting on the chair by her bed, her clothes spread all about her. 'Oh, Orstin, there you are.

I thought you'd found another woman! I need you to pack my bags.' I wondered how she had managed before I arrived in her life, and then thought back to the state of the flat – simple: she hadn't.

By the time we got back to the flat, it was almost midday. Rosebud was bouncing off the walls, excited to see her.

'Oh, my little baby girl. Rosie! Yes, it's Mama! Have you missed your Mama? Yes! Oh, you have? Oh, you pretty little girl.'

Rosie gave Mildred a nip on her thumb with all the excitement. 'Ouch! Rosie! It's your Mama. Bad girl! You must try and take it easy. Shit!'

I stood there shaking my head.

'Orstin, I read in the paper that there is a plug-in one can buy and stick in the electric socket, to calm down a pussy that's over-sexed. Maybe you can ask that lovely female at the chemist.'

I nodded and agreed that I'd ask.

'And I need you to help me wash my hair. Would you be able to do that?' I looked at my watch, wondering if I'd be able to get to the office at all today. 'It itches. I think it's the germs in the hospital.'

Fifteen minutes later we were in the bathroom. I was in my Levis and a white t-shirt. She was splashing water over me like a schoolgirl. 'I never showered together with Geoffrey, but with you, darling, it's fun!'

I got to work at three. I was home again by seven. The TV was blaring out. I rushed for the remote and muted the sound. Mildred was fast asleep in the recliner. She slept again after dinner; I'd made a simple cottage pie.

By quarter to nine, she was ready for bed, and I was not that far behind her.

I managed only a few hours in the office the following day too. Mildred had called. She needed me back at the flat by half-past three. The doctor from Chelsea and Westminster had called just as Resheda had been leaving. A Dr Parsons from her GP surgery was coming to pay her a visit. He wanted to check on her, but more importantly, her meds.

'I'm not sure what one of those female bitches at the hospital has gone and told my surgery, but I'm not taking this lying down.'

By the time I got to the flat, beyond weary, Mildred (dressed in her Norman Hartnell two-piece and wearing her mother's pearls with the amethyst clasp) was ready for war.

'If Parsons is expecting some nice old lady then he is dealing with the wrong broad!'

I calmed her down by suggesting that we wait to see what he actually said. I left my jacket on the library chair and toddled off to the kitchen to make a tray of tea. I'd bought an apricot Swiss roll from Marks & Spencer on my way home. Mildred wouldn't eat any of it.

As I busied myself in the kitchen, Mildred prepared for Dr Parsons by spreading her medication across the dining table.

I let him in. He wasn't much older than me. He was dressed in a blazer, crisp white shirt, tie, and slim chinos. He bounded down the hall like a bunny rabbit, unaware there was a sly old fox waiting eagerly for her prey.

Usually, she'd have insisted on answering the door

herself, facilitating a slow journey along the hall with its photo frames. But there was no time for Hollywood talk today; this was serious, not show business.

She greeted him standing at the head of the table, incandescent as she proudly showed off her wares as if she were about to be awarded the prize for best marrow at the county fair.

Dr Parsons's face said it all. Not only was he horrified at the sheer amount of medication she had been prescribed, but he was shocked that the local pharmacy would allow a patient to stockpile it in such great volumes. He was flabbergasted that she had managed to remain upright while popping so many pills. She, without taking a breath, boasted with great candour about how many she had been swallowing on a daily basis.

Mildred's mood changed as she witnessed his face turn from white to red to scarlet. She protested that he need not worry himself. She took only what she needed – she just needed a lot!

He ordered her to move away from the table and began taking notes on the medication in a small notebook. He separated the pillboxes and cartons into neat piles. He explained that the mountain of meds would do her more harm than good.

Mildred wasn't about to be ordered around. However, realising he was angry, she changed tack. 'Listen, Doctor, I'm a nice old lady who needs to take a pill every once in a while – listen, darlin', I've gotta stay being a swingin' chick! So why don't you come and sit over here and eat cake?'

He ordered her once again to move away from the

237

table. He suggested she could perhaps take a seat herself while he made his audit. I was still standing between the hall and the living room. Parsons had his back to me. He was shaking his head and tutting as he flipped over to a fresh page in his notebook. I jumped as he began directing his conversation at me, determined to know whether the dining table now held the full extent of Mildred's drug collection or if she was hiding a further stash elsewhere in the flat.

I explained that everything she took was usually kept next to her recliner in carrier bags. Mildred interrupted me.

'I took you and that female into my house when you'd no place to go, Orstin! And now you're robbing me of my meds!' she screamed.

Her accusations shocked and saddened me. I tried to calm her down. She pushed me away as she stormed from the living room. Then she turned on her heels and released her anger on the doctor.

'I'm a ninety-three-year-old lady, not some Columbian drug dealer holed up in some slum apartment, for Christ's sake!' she started to howl. 'Oh, if my Baby were only here! I want my Baby!' She fled to her bedroom and slammed the door.

But within minutes Mildred was back in the room, pleading that Parsons go, and pleading that I stay.

It transpired that a doctor at Chelsea and Westminster had told Dr Parsons that he could see from Mildred's charts that she'd been over-medicating. His recommendation, therefore, was that a nurse come in daily to administer Mildred's medication.

If her blood pressure had been high a moment before, it went off the chart at that. She tore at her hair and clothes and ended up catching her necklace; pearls dropped like a hail shower on the parquet floor. It took a brandy to calm her, but it wasn't long before she was on the attack again.

She demanded the doctor pick up the phone to that 'sonna-bitch female' at the hospital and explain that she had made some terrible mistake; that he was with the patient now and could confirm she was clearly fit and very able.

'You are not dealing with some senile old woman, Doctor, who doesn't know her arse from her tit! You're dealing with the daughter of Joseph A. Shay!' she screamed.

With that, she picked up the receiver. 'You can even use my phone, though why I am feeling generous is beyond me.'

Dr Parsons slumped into the library chair and asked that I cut him some cake. 'I've got to give it to you. You don't give up easily,' he murmured.

'Who said I was giving up? I'm not giving an inch.' Mildred raised her glass. 'Now, eat the cake and then dial the hospital.'

Parsons shook his head. 'I'm afraid I can't do that. I wouldn't be doing my job if I were to leave you with all this medication without the proper authority to administer it.'

Mildred grabbed me. 'I have the authority!' she screamed. 'I have Orstin, he knows exactly what I'm to take and when, and besides, some of this stuff I send to my daughter in Hollywood!'

'Jeez…' sighed Parsons, with his mouth full of Swiss roll.

Parsons had a suggestion. He knew a lovely nurse who'd be able to swing by tomorrow, just to sit and talk through her medication. She could bring a blister-pack with its neat little compartments indicating all seven days of the week.

Mildred was not happy, but at least she was calm.

Parsons mopped up the crumbs from his plate. 'Do it for your nephew,' he said, motioning towards me. 'You'll be putting everyone's mind at rest. Why don't you try it for him, if not for yourself?'

I could see Mildred thinking it over. I suspected she was tempted by the idea of a new audience to entertain as often as twice daily.

'What do you say to that?' he asked.

'Yeah, like I need another female who'll be eyeing up all my belongings worth millions, sneaking them out from under my nose while she has me sat on the john waiting for me to do a pee-pee or poo-poo. Fuck!'

I urged Mildred to give it a try. She had other ideas.

'Listen, why don't I ask Resheda? She's the maid Social Services have lumbered me with. I tell you, she can stand by and watch while I take an aspirin.'

Finally, after a further twenty minutes, the doctor left, having booked a nurse to visit for the following day. Much to Mildred's annoyance, he didn't leave empty-handed, but with two large carrier bags full of drugs that he had suggested were close to their use-by date. I walked with him towards the surgery. Mildred had asked me to pick up some new eye drops from the chemist.

'She's a fighter, I'll give her that,' said Parsons with a smile. 'I wish some of my other elderly patients had the same fire in their belly.'

* * *

Mildred had been awake since before sunrise. I was hardly surprised, considering the excitement of the previous day's visit from Dr Parsons. She'd been in bed since before eight; no evening meal, just two bags of Skips and a vodka martini.

The buzzer rang at eight in the morning: Nelly-Lyn from Social Services was on the doorstep. I prayed that Mildred would be at least civil to her. Mildred was dressed in her yellow David Nieper nightie, her face fully made up; the air was thick with attitude, Elnett, and Giorgio Beverly Hills.

Nelly-Lyn was from the Philippines. She was a small woman, perhaps fifty-five. I put out my hand to shake hers. She grabbed mine in both hands and smiled.

'Where is the nice lady?' she beamed.

She followed my lead down the hall. Mildred was almost horizontal in the recliner, her eyes covered with an eye mask. She was ready to give a performance, I could feel it. My heart sank. I wasn't ready for this and neither was Nelly-Lyn.

'Hello, fine lady. I am Nelly-Lyn. I am here to help you, but I think you are probably more inclined to help me.'

Mildred peeled back the eye mask just enough to reveal her right eye. The false eyelashes remained intact.

She groaned that she'd hardly slept, that the visit from Parsons had nearly finished her off.

Mildred wept to the woman about her ordeal with the doctor. She said he'd left her languishing in bed, suffering a nervous breakdown.

Nelly-Lyn knelt on the floor, took both Mildred's hands, and rubbed them gently with her worn thumbs. She reduced Mildred to tears of joy as she praised her strength; moreover, her great beauty and glamour.

The eye-mask off completely, Mildred placed her hand on Nelly-Lyn's cheek. 'I know you're lying, darling, but I love it,' she whispered. 'At this rate, you'll have me beat.'

'I don't want to beat you, nice lady,' said Nelly-Lyn, still holding Mildred's hand. 'I want you as bright as a shiny button so you and your handsome friend here can go about doing things and not have to worry about medication.'

I left them to it: Mildred directing Nelly-Lyn to her stash, stuffed in bags beside the recliner. Together they decanted them into the plastic box.

I kissed Mildred goodbye and thanked Nelly-Lyn. I darted down the hall and into my bedroom to grab my coat from my unmade bed.

I paused. I was sure I'd made the bed earlier. I pulled back the duvet: there, sprawled out from one end of the double bed to the other, were giant boxes of Rennies, two extra-large bottles of Gaviscon, dozens of packets of aspirin and paracetamol, and two cartons of antihistamines.

Mildred might have finally been willing to play ball,

but as I stared down at the hoard, it was obvious she wasn't planning to play entirely fair.

Fourteen

The Comeback

While Joanna had been away, the routine to prepare Mildred for each new day had fallen to me. The day before, Mildred had made me help settle her in the recliner to watch *Murder, She Wrote* while her feet were soaking in a red bucket, in order to soften her toenails before a home pedicure. To be honest, I didn't mind – Mildred could ill afford a chiropodist.

My mother had been horrified when Joanna had let slip that I'd been cutting Mildred's toenails. She had thought such an act not suitable for a young man, and certainly not for her son.

'I think the time has come to investigate nice care homes for Mildred.' Mother and her friends Rosemary and Monica felt that, as Joanna and I were soon to be married, and especially now that Joanna was hardly ever at the flat, the time had come for me to move on.

I had consoled Mother by telling her that the mornings had been quieter – Mildred stayed in bed longer. Mother had rolled her eyes. 'Nobody likes a martyr, darling.'

Dad had backed Mother up with a 'hear, hear'.

Mildred's moods seemed to fluctuate rapidly. One minute she'd be talking about Father Cherry with great serenity; the next, attacking with great venom the performance of an actress on *Eastenders*. Then there was her devious behaviour during the visits from Nelly-Lyn.

And on top of all this, my work hadn't been going well. My boss was cross with me for constantly leaving my desk to dash to an emergency. He had said he'd have to look at me making up my hours. He'd even called Marigold from HR to join us. When I had seen Marigold, my heart sank. She and I hadn't ever hit it off; and furthermore, Marigold, unlike my other colleagues, thought it wrong that Joanna and I lived with Mildred. She'd told Marina that she thought us a pair of 'freeloaders'.

Marigold had grinned as she produced a long list of dates on which she estimated I'd either arrived late, left early, or not come in at all. By the time Marigold and her colleague Stefan, whom she'd asked to join us, had gone through the list, I'd hardly any holiday left for the year.

* * *

Joanna had come back from 'the country'. The reason was our visit to the Cavalry and Guards Club that night, so that Mildred could 'treat the cook': a thank-you to Joanna for all her hard work shopping and cooking – even though it had been months now since she left, leaving me as cook, cleaner, PA, and much in between.

The run-up to this evening had seen Joanna helping Mildred to get ready. With Mildred less and less dexterous, Joanna had painted her nails and coiffured Mildred's big blonde hair.

Mildred delighted in seeing Joanna back in the flat. Hearing them giggle, one would have thought they were best friends; in truth, Joanna had never stopped trying to get on with Mildred. I thought Mildred was still feeling guilty about her continued jibes at Joanna. I wondered if Joanna wouldn't just come out and tell Mildred that she had been looking for jobs in hospitality for me in Gloucestershire. I was on tenterhooks and remained so throughout the dinner.

As the widow of Captain Geoffrey Steele of the First Royal Dragoons, Mildred had life membership to the Cavalry and Guards Club. But before we had come along, she'd abandoned the institution, only having ventured in perhaps two dozen times since Geoffrey's death.

The club was Mildred's last bastion of luxury. Although she could ill afford it, Mildred had always picked up the tab for either intimate luncheons or larger parties for her ever-dwindling band of acquaintances, mostly from the War days: Roger Mellor Makins (the son of Mildred and Geoffrey's great chum, Brigadier-General Sir Ernest Makins) and Rafaelle, Duchess of Leinster included. When the money had gone, the soirées stopped, and not one of her friends ever returned the favour.

She particularly liked being at the club just before Christmas; there was perhaps the most elegant "all you can eat" buffet I ever enjoyed.

Joanna and I followed Mildred into the club; she asked that we allow her to walk through the front door unaided. She didn't want the staff to think she had become 'an old crone'. Two steps behind, we watched as she swept through. A gentleman behind the desk welcomed her, and another took her hand as she moved gingerly in three-inch heels towards him. A lady in her mid-sixties came over.

'Madame,' she said, 'we've missed you!' The scene was akin to the return of Norma Desmond to Paramount Studios in the film *Sunset Boulevard*.

Mildred was happy to, in her words, 'have the old gang back together'. Moreover, she was touched that the staff at the club hadn't forgotten her. There was even interest from a new admirer, much to the delight of Joanna.

Mildred had clocked him in the Ladies' Coffee Room where we had enjoyed pre-dinner drinks. As we went into the restaurant and were shown our table, Joanna also noticed him sitting with another gentleman close by.

Charles Morris introduced himself as we perused the dessert menu, only leaving when our puddings arrived. He was tall, with neat white hair and a moustache. Joanna suggested to Mildred that perhaps he could become a new friend. Initially, Mildred thought so too. As we ate, Mildred continually looked over to where he sat dining with 'his Old Etonian chum', and asked Joanna for a running commentary on what Joanna could hear of their conversation.

The gentlemen both wished us an enjoyable remainder of our evening before they left. Mildred looked Charles up and down like a searchlight. Her attention was drawn to his ankles.

'Bicycle clips!' he exclaimed. 'I've got my bicycle outside.'

'Oh, really,' said Mildred, as she stared at the bicycle clips and then at Charles' face. 'Tell me, don't you possess a car?'

It turned out Charles did have a car, a BMW, but after a prang on Piccadilly outside Fortnum & Mason, he had decided his driving days were over. He'd opted to use his old bicycle or, in inclement weather, took the number 38 bus. The look on Mildred's face told Joanna and me that he'd rapidly gone down in her estimation.

Mildred did, however, give Charles her card. He never called, but she and I did see him again. I pointed him out to Mildred as he approached us on his bicycle later that month, riding down Ebury Street. Mildred's wave withered as she and I noticed one very large testicle hanging out and swinging low from his short shorts.

'Oh, Gawd!' she said, glad he hadn't noticed us. 'I haven't seen a pair of balls like that since I got fresh with Frank Sinatra!'

The next time we were at the Cavalry and Guards, I recognised Charles' friend and enquired after him. He'd actually died some weeks before, while on a tandem holiday in Eastbourne. When I told Mildred that Charles Morris was no more, she looked forlorn, but soon lightened the mood: 'What a waste of all that throbbing muscle!' she laughed as she shrugged her shoulders.

* * *

It was Joanna who broke first, kneeling in front of Mildred in the recliner the morning after the club. Joanna hadn't found the appropriate moment the previous night to reveal her plans for a new life for the both of us, so had left it until the morning.

Mildred stroked Joanna's hair. Joanna was crying, with her head resting on Mildred's lap. But Mildred only had eyes for me.

Her greatest fear, ever since we had first arrived, had been that one day we would leave. Drying her eyes, Joanna told Mildred of the opportunities that a job as a hotel manager would provide for me. There would be a country retreat for Mildred too, as Joanna was moving back into her cottage; Rachael and Jason were moving to fresh pastures in the town. I didn't think Mildred was taking any of it in. Her eyes were fixed on me. She asked over and over, 'You'll not go? You're not leaving me? Oh, Christ, oh, God, you're not leaving me?'

Later that night, with Joanna in bed and Mildred in her room, I sat in the library chair and read quietly. My 'me-time' was soon interrupted. Mildred appeared at the living room door.

'I'm warning you, Orstin,' she said, wagging her finger at me. 'Don't lock yourself away in the fucking forest, for Christ's sake! You're only a kid, and besides the occasional tumble with the female, there'll not be a thing in the woods that'll stimulate you. You'll be alone and lost like a God-damn hobbit.' I ended up promising that I wouldn't leave her.

* * *

I woke early; Mildred was already in the living room drinking tea. Joanna had promised lunch out as a treat today, and tonight the three of us were joining Howard for a private view of Robert Rankin's photographic work at the Alex Proud Gallery in Camden.

Mildred told me she was going to skip lunch. She hadn't any appetite. She'd tell Joanna when she woke. Perhaps she could palm her off by suggesting Joanna invite the nice exotic-looking girl Joanna had introduced her to a few weeks ago, the 'female' she'd studied with. Saddened Mildred had blown her off, Joanna sent Shehnaz a text message.

Despite my solemn vow that I was going nowhere, Mildred remained glum. As the day wore on, Mildred grew increasingly unimpressed with the idea of visiting Camden; she rarely ventured beyond SW1.

Mildred disappeared into her bedroom and emerged a short while later in one of the David Nieper numbers, which had benefitted greatly from a spin in the washing machine. Sitting in the recliner, her right marabou slipper tilting off her big toe, Mildred planned her television viewing for the night. She would not be moved.

After several attempts to change Mildred's mind, we headed off for lunch in Sloane Square alone.

It was Howard who finally coaxed Mildred into a night out. She spent the rest of the afternoon preparing herself, trying on various outfits before settling on a simple black skirt, red jacket, mink coat, and hat; her discarded clothes were left piled high on her bed.

We took my car to Camden; I was at the wheel,

Mildred was beside me, and Howard and Joanna were in the back of the VW Golf.

For Howard, used to celebrity drinks parties and gallery openings, the launch of Rankin's new book was just another night out. I knew nothing about the photographer besides recognising his numerous shots of models for fashion magazines. Once we were inside, however, it became clear that he also had a passion for nudes – and lots of them, particularly women, or women's genitalia to be exact.

A tall black twenty-something male offered Mildred a drink. She eagerly accepted, taking a large slug as she turned to Joanna. 'Oh, Gawd, darling, don't look at the wall behind you, dear – it's full of hairy cunts!'

Still anxious that I might leave (despite my promises not to), she decided to console herself with more liquor than usual. Her half-empty glass was perpetually replenished by the gallery staff.

The exhibition of *The Nude Photography of Rankin* had been much applauded, according to an attractive PR girl called Sara Vaughn. She told us that he was a genius for featuring 'real women' and not simply supermodels. Mildred looked about the room at the gargantuan black and white close-ups. 'You don't say,' she muttered, as she handed her empty glass to me.

Mildred was soon making herself heard. She wasn't against nude photography, although she asked Sara and Joanna if they wouldn't have liked to have seen 'just a little bit of cock, for Christ's sake' amongst all the female genitalia. Mildred moaned to writer and fashion journalist Judith Watt that she found the subjects unattractive, failing to understand the concept of 'real people'. Soon Mildred was drawing others in, voicing her distaste. 'Gawd,' she grimaced to Nicky Haslam, Amanda Donahue, and *The Daily Telegraph*'s fashion editor Hilary Alexander, 'the Great British public can be so darn common!'

Joanna and I felt it was perhaps time we left, but Mildred was determined to stay and provided her own personal critique to anyone in the crowd who'd listen. However much Joanna and I tried to hush her up, she continued her crusade. 'That one with the bruised legs looks like a medical experiment! And that one is so ugly!' Mildred finally caught the eye of a young guy in a trilby and, pointing to a display cabinet, said, 'Honey, don't look in there, it's full of twats!' Donahue and Haslam heard and laughed.

'Darlings, I've been in Hollywood with some of the biggest dicks in the business, but never with this many cunts!' Rankin himself was drawn to Haslam's loud laugh. He listened patiently.

Mildred raised her eyebrows and knocked back her third glass of wine as he explained his work. 'But honestly, darling, where are all the cocks?'

'I've shot plenty of cock,' he said as he took hold of her hand. 'But the world is afraid of male nudes and everybody is scared of willies.'

'Afraid of willies!' she roared. 'Honey, I love 'em! Listen, show me yours and I wouldn't scream one bit!'

Rankin kissed her on the cheek and escaped into the crowd. Howard found Mildred a chair and another drink. Still unimpressed, she grew tired of the evening:

the music, the laughter, and the atmosphere all became like a garbled racket to Mildred, the buzz of her hearing aids competing with the crowd.

Spying a small bank of photographers upon our exit, she lingered long enough to have her photo taken with Amanda Donahue. She was elated when Amanda told the press, 'This is what a real Hollywood star looks like!' Mildred was soon quizzing Amanda on working with Oliver Reed.

With her arm around Mildred, Amanda proceeded to tell her that Reed was intimidating. 'Oh, he was?' said Mildred. 'So were Johnny Weissmuller and Errol Flynn, honey.'

Amanda gave Mildred a quizzical look as Mildred continued, 'I never drank a thing in Hollywood, not a drop, only milk. I was called 'Hollywood's Pocket Venus'.' Mildred glared over at me, and Joanna on my arm, laughing with a male photographer. Joanna noticed Mildred's icy stare now too – she pulled me closer. Mildred, still with Amanda Donohue, asked for another glass of wine. She snarled.

'I tell you something, Amanda, I was never intimidated by any muscle either!'

* * *

The Christmas holidays proved to be just the break I needed. Joanna and I spent the entire time with her parents, or else nestled in the cottage with a roaring fire and our own decorated Christmas tree.

An old friend of Mildred's called Timothy had rung to ask if Mildred would like to spend the holiday with him at his country estate in Staffordshire. Mildred thought it perfect – that is until I told her I'd not be joining her.

Mildred had then rung Howard. She'd figured that because Howard was single he'd happily 'go with'.

'Think of it,' she'd said to me. 'If the brother got with Timothy, we would all have a nice mansion we could live in.' But Howard already had plans.

Annoyed at being stood up by both her 'bricks', she initially sulked and suggested to me as late as December 23rd that she'd be staying put alone in the flat. That night Timothy rang to say he'd be collecting Mildred in his navy-blue Rolls-Royce. I spent the run-up to Christmas helping her pack.

What did happen over those holidays was that Joanna withdrew her suggestion that I should leave London. She'd come to realise how dependent Mildred really was. For the time being, I'd be staying at the flat during the week, in the Forest of Dean on weekends, and – as long as I didn't take any more unauthorised days off – in my job. I left Joanna and the cottage on New Year's Day – once again, long-distance lovers.

* * *

The start to the New Year seemed relatively calm. Howard called to ask if I'd like some extra work for an event he was staging for De Beers in LA. It would include invitations to numerous parties during the Oscars season. I jumped at the opportunity. The idea of being in LA in February was so tempting.

As I thought it through, I became suddenly less jubilant; my mind turned to Mildred and who'd look after her in my absence. Joanna was in the midst of term-time, so no hope there. My mother wouldn't leave Dad – not that I could imagine her handling Mildred. My thoughts turned to Julie, but I soon realised she'd be busy looking after Minnie and Ben. Mildred's few friends declined. I tried Timothy; he said he'd happily entertain Mildred again – next year.

I suddenly thought of Resheda and decided I'd try her. She and I were becoming quite friendly, even though Mildred warned me to keep conversation down to a bare minimum. 'She could call the Feds about you staying here,' said Mildred, watching from her recliner as Resheda dusted her knick-knacks at the far end of the living room. 'I don't like it that she has something on me – imagine if I got busted by the social security people.'

I calmed her by arguing that I was providing a service to the council by minimising her reliance on the NHS and keeping calls to the doctor to a minimum. Mildred hadn't called for an ambulance at all so far that year – an impressive achievement, since it was February 1st.

Inga Schmidt said rather sarcastically that flashing blue lights were a more regular occurrence outside the Cundy Street flats than the full moon. I told her Mildred was lonely, to which Inga retorted that lonely people should stick together in nursing homes. Never all that keen on her, I was much less of a fan after that. Inga continued to complain to me outside the lift on the ground floor about the volume of Mildred's television, her noisy 'grinding' shower, and repugnant pop music. I said that I hoped she never found herself in the same predicament, unwell and on her own.

With new Christmas-gift additions from IKEA (a standard lamp that worked, a more comfortable sofa, and blinds for the dining room windows) the flat was looking quite smart. As I was taking care of Mildred's laundry, Resheda had been cleaning for a whole hour every Thursday morning. I'd given her Joanna's old Walkman. She delighted in listening to it whilst she vacuumed and dusted, changed Mildred's bedding, and washed the kitchen floor. Mildred asked what she was listening to. Mildred told me she was surprised an 'Arab lady' should be keen on Western music. I told her Resheda had lived in the West for a long time. 'So had Rachmaninoff, darling,' said Mildred, 'but try and get him to listen to anything fresh and modern like Gershwin – impossible!'

When Resheda arrived early on Thursday she greeted Mildred warmly before plugging herself into her music. Mildred talked at her regardless. When Resheda left, Mildred told me she wanted to know exactly what the cleaner was listening to. She'd noticed Resheda's mouth moving a lot.

'Perhaps she's communicating with Social Services,' said Mildred anxiously.

I agreed with Mildred, jokingly comparing Resheda to Bond villain Rosa Klebb. Mildred didn't see the funny side. I decided not to ask Resheda to keep an eye on Mildred. Instead, I'd speak to Larry.

I was preparing dinner when Howard called. Mildred answered the phone. I heard her voice rise to an unmeasurable decibel as she squealed with glee. I stood before her with a potato in one hand and a peeler in the other.

'Oh, darling,' she said, exuberant. 'Cissie Shay is gonna come and play with you boys in Hollywood!'

I wasn't sure how my face looked. After a while, Mildred asked if I'd cut myself on 'that thing that's not a knife' as she pointed to the potato peeler. She got to her feet.

'Oh, darling, I know, I'm kinda speechless too – isn't it marvellous?' she said.

I was still standing in the doorway. I registered I was speaking but the words didn't make sense. Mildred rationalised my behaviour as suppressed exhilaration. She led me to the library chair. I sat as she reached for her well-thumbed medical book. Kicked back in the recliner, Mildred speculated on what was troubling me. She'd thought many times that my being 'an obituary man' wasn't good for my health. She forbade me ever to use her name when penning my tributes to any of her former co-stars. 'It's a bad omen, dahling, and I ain't going no-place!'

Mildred wondered if I was off-colour as Joanna was away and I was not being fulfilled in the bedroom.

'My darling Geoffrey and I had sex every morning,' said Mildred wistfully as she checked facts in her medical book. 'When I couldn't offer myself to him he found different avenues, but he always came back to me.' She giggled. 'I won't tell if you won't.'

I tried to convince Mildred I was fine. She disagreed and planned to call Lady Janet or Caroline, Duchess of Leeds.

'What for?' I asked.

'To see if you'd be able to meet with their daughters or nieces,' she said, looking up from the book. Mildred was sure that whilst Joanna was 'playing schools in the country' I needed stimulation.

* * *

Howard convinced me that he'd take the full burden of Mildred in LA. Two days later, he arrived at the flat with airline tickets and a schedule. Mildred was so excited at the prospect of returning to Hollywood that she had to take sleeping pills every night for a fortnight in the run-up to our departure.

For an entire week, Mildred had been pampering herself, with a visit to Michelle Jones and a manicure. Mildred astounded me when, on a rare shopping trip that week, she asked Howard to accompany her to MAC Cosmetics. The shop staff were bemused and sold her over eighty pounds' worth of cosmetics. 'Don't tell Baby,' she made him promise, immediately feeling guilty. 'I shouldn't have done that.' He, Joanna, and I often encouraged Mildred to spend, and on occasions she did.

The next issue was what she would wear for Oscars night.

I rang Sara Vaughn and, with her black book of fashion contacts, she had just the solution: the designer Eric

Way. An emergency appointment was made and Eric, Sara, and her dachshund Twiglet visited the flat.

I was in the kitchen making tea when they arrived. I heard Mildred 'talk Hollywood'. With tea cups on a tray and Mildred's silver tea set polished, I stood and served. Eric was perched on the edge of a chair, rubbing one hand in thought along the edge of a long-since-perished antimacassar, and with the other producing a sketch of a dress suitable for Mildred to be seen wearing on the red carpet.

In quick time, Eric designed an exquisite midnight-blue satin dress with a delicate Chantilly lace overcoat covered in Swarovski crystals. Eric and Sara quickly became Mildred's new best friends. Later, when Mildred discovered Eric's clients included Cherie Blair, Ivana Trump, and Shirley Bassey, Mildred joked with friends, 'You mean Mr Way hasn't designed a dress for you? Oh, really, darling, he is a must.'

* * *

In the Forest of Dean, the weekend following our return from LA, I recounted the experience. Mildred had lapped up every moment of her week's stay; jet-lag did nothing to diminish her vigour. She rose at five on the first morning for an interview Howard had orchestrated at eight with *The LA Times*. Sporting dark glasses and wearing the Made in England suit, she sat in her suite at the W Hotel in Westwood, shamelessly name-dropping – the old stories were a sensation to fresh ears. She drank champagne at pre-Oscar parties, and while at

The Standard one night, she got behind the bar to show a handsome black bar steward how to fix a 'real' vodka martini. I watched as she flirted with him.

'Oh, boy, he's a real doll,' Mildred said as she returned to her seat, waving back at him every now and then. Then, at a huge party in Beverly Hills, Joan Rivers and her daughter Melissa stopped Mildred and, with microphone in hand, asked what she thought of the new generation of Hollywood stars. 'What do you think of J-Lo?' Rivers asked. I stood next to Mildred as she grimaced.

'J-Lo? I mean, darling, that woman built her career on having an arse!' With that, Mildred span round and, tilting forward, gave her own rump a firm smack. 'I mean, darling, I've got an arse!'

She dined out on the fact that Sharon Stone, on stage at a photography event celebrating the work of paparazzo Frank Worth, had mouthed the words, 'you are beautiful' to her, and on the same night she had met James Woods and Christian Slater, who seemed to beam when she walked into the room.

The week's festivities culminated in a lavish dinner in honour of Elizabeth Taylor in Bel-Air. I sat at Mildred's table with Laura Elena Harding and a handsome fifty-something man with greying hair. Mildred had spotted him earlier in the evening, lounging by the swimming pool. During dinner, Mildred was delighted to see the same man was seated to her right. He rose as she drew close. Batting her eyelashes, she gave him a slow sexy look. Her performance was priceless.

He introduced himself as Hector, a banker. 'Oh!' said Mildred. 'You're my kinda fella. You got any samples?'

There was no doubting her sparkle and appeal. She entertained the table with her Hollywood tales and silenced them all with her story of the attempted rape by Errol Flynn, before lightening the mood and showing off a white sapphire – a personal gift from Harry Winston.

Halfway through the main course, Mildred got up from her chair and walked over to Elizabeth herself.

'You wouldn't remember Mildred Shay, would you?' she asked. Elizabeth Taylor looked Mildred straight in the eye, tossed her head back, and gave that familiar cackle-like laugh of hers. Holding Mildred's hand, she said softly, 'And why wouldn't I remember Mildred Shay?' and then kissed her.

Ecstatic, Mildred all but danced back to the table, tears in her eyes. 'She was so happy,' I told Joanna later.

Mildred drowned in champagne that night, finally taking to her bed at three in the morning with a cocktail of aspirin and Nytol.

I missed Joanna so much during the trip. Being in California while she was in England made me realise how much I loved her. Mildred sensed this. As she drifted off to sleep while I packed the clothes sprawled all about her suite on our last evening in California, she whispered in semi-consciousness:

'Why don't you and I get married instead? I've got rich friends and have the right address in London and we have fun, don't we, and I love you and all that's missing is the sex.'

Mildred never mentioned the conversation again.

Yet as the weeks went on, Mildred grew ever more anxious that I should marry Joanna.

Caught as I was between them both, my head was ready to explode. My life became increasingly unbearable. When Joanna did come back to the flat on odd weekends, Mildred initially backed down, allowing us time together. But by Saturday afternoon, she would begin to demand my attention, which resulted in Joanna retreating, as she'd done before, to the portable TV in the bedroom, rather than listening to any more Hollywood stories. I'd spend most of those evenings in the hall, flitting between one or the other of them.

On one such weekend, Joanna and I made the most of being in the city together. We walked miles hand-in-hand through London, ending up at the Southbank. Unbeknown to Joanna, Mildred rang my mobile fourteen times, trying to tell me her breaking news.

Mildred's Hollywood career – such as it was – meant everything to her. She'd retained her agent to the bitter end. The phone hadn't rung once in all the time I'd known her and then, quite suddenly, just when Joanna and I were enjoying our day together whilst Mildred ate her peanut butter and apricot sandwiches in front of *Murder, She Wrote*, the phone did ring. June Epstein had received a call from the producers of the stage revival of *When Harry Met Sally*. They wanted to test Mildred for the role of the restaurant customer who said the line 'I'll have what she's having' – the most memorable dialogue in the production.

Joanna and I were back at the flat when the script arrived. Mildred banished the TV to our room in preparation for the casting call on Friday. Mildred asked

Joanna and then me to help her with her lines. But however hard she tried, Mildred just couldn't get them right. Exhausted by Thursday night, Joanna sloped off to bed as I stayed up till dawn with Mildred. The read-through was hours away.

Intent on making Mildred look current, Joanna dressed her in a pair of her Levis, a zebra-print scarf (a gift from Joanna's mother), and a pair of black and white patent leather shoes that Howard had bought her. Mildred admired herself in the full-length mirror on the back of the wardrobe door in our room, satisfied she'd be making a comeback.

The aroma of Wild Fig by Jo Malone lingered long after she'd left the flat in a car sent by the producer.

With me at work and Joanna shopping with Shehnaz for the day, we didn't meet up until seven. We had dinner out and it was half-past nine by the time we got back to the flat.

What we discovered was both a tragic and pitiful sight. Mildred had received the phone call saying she hadn't got the job literally as we walked through the door. Her anguish was painful to watch. Like a child, she screamed and screamed. With one determined yank, she ripped the phone from its socket and threw it at the wall in a fit of rage. The very idea that she couldn't secure even a meagre bit part was too much to bear. She pushed past us to the bathroom, where she threw up, and then hurried into the make-up room. She grabbed handfuls of cosmetics and threw what she could at her reflection in the mirror, the scent of Lily of the Valley and lavender face power filling the air. She ran down the hall and pulled at her hair, wailing like a banshee. Her mood remained the same all week after Joanna had returned to Gloucestershire.

Mildred languished in her dressing gown in the recliner, weeping to people over the phone. By the following week, she had taken to her pills and her bed, calling the Belgravia surgery for a doctor. The following week she began ringing friends like Zsa Zsa Gabor, Shirley Chambers, Glenn Ford, her priest, and Mrs Patel at the chemist, to say she'd had a lucky escape as the play was bound to flop anyway.

Baby called with her condolences. She doubted her mother could manage the demanding schedule of up to twelve performances a week; furthermore, she suggested the money would be crap for such a small bit-part.

It was Mildred's agent, June Epstein, who shone a light on what had actually happened. It was at a small gathering of her aged clients at her flat, a month after the audition.

Sitting around her small dining table, I watched and listened to June, Mildred, a kindly elderly gentleman by the name of Victor, Cicely Paget-Bowman, and the director Alan Charlesworth, who'd once cast Mildred in *Before Waterlilies* for the BBC *Play for Today* opposite Carmen Silvera.

The scene reminded me of the waxworks in Billy Wilder's *Sunset Boulevard*, with Mildred looking every bit like a former film star, dressed in a black lace cocktail dress with a pink shrug, fox fur, and a rather decrepit Lilly Daché hat that had belonged to her mother.

Drinking from a wonderfully old-fashioned champagne 'pond', she dominated the conversation.

Mildred talked at her audience, declaring that *Before Waterlilies* absolutely should have been her comeback. A solid starring role on the BBC that she had hoped would bring her to the attention of producers – 'even Hollywood'.

Suffice to say, she and Carmen didn't get on. The fallout that ensued convinced Mildred that despite her 'marvellous performance', Carmen was so jealous that she made sure Mildred was blacklisted from the BBC. Carmen was just about to secure a role that would give her everlasting fame as Madame Edith, the long-suffering wife of café owner René on *Allo! Allo!*

Mildred was convinced that Carmen suffered an inferiority complex because she had to share a dressing room with someone from Hollywood. Her soliloquy ended with Mildred's reminiscence of having to catch a bus to the studio after Carmen ordered their driver to leave without Mildred from the bed and breakfast where the two actresses were staying.

As I helped June to some more wine, she sighed that it was Mildred who had been the cause of the tension. It was then that she told me about the problem during the audition for *When Harry Met Sally*.

'Even before she'd spoken a line of dialogue, dear Mildred pulled from her handbag her Hollywood bumf – you know, photographs taken a million years ago of her with old Hollywood stars,' June told me. 'Well, Austin, these young co-stars like that nice boy from *Baywatch*, Luke Perry – they had no idea who she was talking about and Mildred got a bit irritated.'

What was so upsetting for June was the fact that Mildred hadn't been able to remember the line. June poured a glass of wine for me and topped herself up as well.

'You know what hurt?' asked June. 'Mildred wanted that part for Baby, so it could potentially lead to more work.'

There would be one final hurrah.

Fifteen

The Photoshoot

*B*uoyed by the glamour after our return from Los Angeles, Mildred had felt quite well, making only occasional calls to her GP. Things changed rapidly.

Mildred began to spend more time at the Chelsea and Westminster hospital than she did at home. She blamed her ill health on her heartache at not managing the comeback she had so desperately craved, coupled with continued trouble with the cat. The latest battle commenced during a long petting session when, according to Mildred, Rosie became excited and over-sexed. The result was that she attacked Mildred's face with astonishing power and left her with a bleeding nose. Having only just been released from the hospital that morning, that afternoon Mildred and I were back.

Anxious and upset after two hospital visits in quick succession, Mildred told me in the waiting room that the last time she'd felt the same level of vulnerability, the same level of despair, was in 1968, sitting behind the wheel of her Corvette at stoplights on the Sunset Strip, her mother next to her in the passenger seat.

Through tears, Mildred recounted how Lillian Shay had turned to her and said she missed her baby son Arnold deeply.

'I reached for Mother's hand – she pulled away,' sniffed Mildred. 'Mother launched into a tirade of abuse. Eventually, she told me that she wished it had been me and not Arnold knocked down and killed beside the ice truck.'

Mildred never saw her mother again. Lillian died six weeks later, at home with Adeline by her side.

It was this heartache that sent Mildred searching for meditation and calm at Joshua Tree. Her religious faith, she confided, suffered a breakdown. She pulled a small Bible from her handbag – her faith was now strong in the face of new adversities.

But it soon became clear there was something else wrong, something more serious than the career disappointment and the scratches. As she was being checked over, a nurse with a soft Scottish accent asked whether she felt any pain.

'I live with pain!' exclaimed Mildred. 'My heavenly daughter Baby lives thousands of miles from her Mama in Hollywood, and now my other baby – my cat – she hates me!' Mildred took my hand. 'I blame Rosebud's anger on my friend here.' She swallowed hard. 'I tell ya, it's hard for a mother to admit this, but I think my pussy's a lesbian.' Mildred squeezed my hand harder. 'Sorry, kiddo, she's the opposite of me – she hates men.'

Mildred asked the nurse as she took her blood pressure whether she thought the same as Lady Janet: that her pussy was over-sexed. The nurse was sure that that wasn't the case, and that both her daughter and her cat were simply devoted. The nurse (her badge read Jude) asked more questions. After two hours, Jude suggested that Mildred see a specialist. Mildred remained in hospital for the next five days for a series of scans and a lumbar puncture.

I collected her from the hospital on Thursday night. She was still in bed when I put my coat on to leave for the office on Friday morning. I popped my head round the door. She was reading from her prayer book, but she said her left eye hurt. She blamed her landlord, the Duke of Westminster, for not arranging good enough lighting in her apartment.

'That Duke, I tell you, he's onto me. He sees I'm not paying a fortune in rent like some of these newbies moving in, so little by little he is trying to move me out – he's tampered with my light bulbs and the electric current for my new expensive television set!'

On closer inspection, I noticed her eye had turned inwards. Mildred asked me for a mirror.

'Oh, Christ!' she yelled. 'I'm fucking cross-eyed like the queen bee at Metro-Goldwyn-Mayer, Norma Shearer!'

I rang Joanna on the way to work and told her I was worried. She reluctantly admitted I should stay in London with Mildred this weekend, just to observe her.

* * *

Howard came for dinner a few days later. Unable to get hold of me, Mildred had called him in hysterics, saying that Larry had been forbidden by nurses at the GP surgery to collect and deliver her medication. He'd spoken to Mildred's surgery and had been informed that they were concerned that 'the old lady' was over-medicating again, despite Nelly-Lyn administering her pills. Larry explained to Howard that the nurses wondered if overdoses might have caused the paralysis of her eye. Powerless to calm her, Howard rang Father Cherry and asked him to visit. For now, Howard told me, Mildred was praying with Father Cherry in her living room and, if not happy, she was perhaps more peaceful.

Changing the subject away from hospitals and doctors, Howard announced during pudding that he'd been approached by Alison Booth, the editor of the *Orient Express Magazine*, to help style and cast the twenty-first-anniversary issue. His idea was to recreate Agatha Christie's famous murder mystery.

The following week, after he'd managed to get Alison to agree to a small budget to engage my services, Howard rang me with ideas. We settled on a five-page fashion spread, a contemporary twist with current fashion trends.

Through his ever-growing network of fashion and film contacts, Howard accessed a wide range of actors and actresses. Joan Collins was interested but likely to be in the south of France; Sally Hawkins was intrigued but unable to commit, as was Ioan Gruffield.

Jeremy Sheffield, Stefan Booth, Amanda Donohue, Diana Rigg's daughter Rachael Sterling, Claire Grogan, Geoffrey Hutchings, Richard Shelton, Rita Tushingham, and Ron Moody all confirmed. The only one left to cast was Princess Dragomiroff. The shoot was due to take place in three weeks' time.

Howard stayed with Mildred for the first three days of July as Joanna and I visited friends Bertie and Nicola in Hove. Howard rang me to say Mildred was thrilled to have received our wedding invitation for September 3rd, but anxious all over again that I would be leaving for good. I shared Mildred's fears with Joanna. Nicola joked that perhaps Joanna should return to London and we could live as a married couple with Mildred. Joanna had her heart set on my moving to the Forest by winter. Sensing an argument, Bertie moved the conversation on.

Back in Belgravia, Howard consoled Mildred by telling her that if I went, he'd stay. He said it was the happiest he'd seen her. But he was worried. He sensed she was off colour – for real.

By the time I returned to London, it was becoming clear that Mildred the firecracker was starting to lose her snap. Becoming frailer following a week's stay at The Royal Eye Hospital in Marylebone, the side of her face appeared to be falling and her eye refused to rectify itself. She was taken in to spend the next two days at the Chelsea and Westminster.

* * *

I had been waiting for a bus to get to the hospital for over forty minutes. The air was filled with the sound of sirens. Eventually, I gave up on the bus and walked to the hospital. It was not until I arrived and saw the news reports in the waiting room that it became clear there had been a terrorist attack on the capital. When I reached the Adele Dixon ward, Mildred was glued to the news, other patients cuddled around her.

With tears in her eyes, she embraced me and asked me to phone Howard and that nice Corinne and Kirsty to make sure they were safe.

We left the hospital at six-thirty with a large bag of medication which she had hidden amongst her under-wear in her overnight bag. She warned me not to men-tion the stash to 'those bitches' at her surgery. When we got to the flat, she dragged the suitcase to the bathroom and pulled out ancient bottles, tubs, and jars in order to make room for her hoard.

'Nothing, I say *nothing*, is going to come between me and these meds.' Mildred meant business.

Later that night, Francesca Hilton called. Her moth-er Zsa Zsa Gabor had suffered a serious stroke. 'As if this day could get any worse,' cried Mildred. She added Zsa Zsa to her prayer list that night.

After the debacle at the doctor's surgery, the eye con-dition, and the news of her friend's illness, we deemed it insensitive to ask Mildred if she'd like to play the exotic and aged Princess Dragomiroff.

Howard spent the next few nights at the flat, during which time he talked enthusiastically about the forth-coming *Orient Express* shoot with me.

A few days later Mildred abruptly became interested in the project. In the recliner, watching the blaring tele-vision, she miraculously heard Howard mention that he had been thinking of Peggy Cummins, the star of *Gun Crazy*, to be cast at the Princess.

'I know that name!' cried Mildred.

'Peggy Cummins. Yes, Cissie, she was in Film Noir films and at Twentieth Century Fox during the forties.'

'Oh, she was…' Mildred was silent for a moment. 'Oh, Orstin, how old is the Cummins female?'

'Peggy Cummins is years younger than you, Cissie!' I laughed. 'She's almost eighty, I guess.'

'Shit! I don't wanna hear about people who are younger than me,' she barked.

Howard offered Mildred a glass of wine. She'd had a glass with her meal, veal with dauphinoise potato. She declined; she told us in great detail how the food mixed with her pain meds for her sore eye had messed with her bowel movements. Moments later she suggested perhaps a small vodka martini. Howard was in the kitchen when Mildred got up from the recliner to join me at the table.

'Listen, Orstin, Peggy Cummins was never a big star. Why, I can't even think of one of her pictures. No, she's no good, darling.' Mildred pulled a dining chair from under the table and sat next to me. 'Orstin, is there some kind of reason why your brother has decided to not ask me?' she said, watching the door to make sure he wasn't there – but she was whispering so loudly I knew he could hear her.

I explained that he had thought of her from the get-go, but as she had been unwell he didn't want to place any sort of anxiety on her. I also named some of Peggy's fine performances opposite co-stars such as Rex Harrison, Edward G. Robinson, and Sean Connery. This all fell on deaf ears.

'Peggy Cummins just isn't right, darling,' she said, reaching for her drink. 'No, she's not a good choice – no, definitely not the Cummins woman.' She finished her drink. 'Now, be honest, who else has he asked?'

She pooh-poohed Muriel Pavlow as being too slight, laughed at the mention of Betsy Drake, saying she was nothing more than the wife of Cary Grant and no actress, declared she had never truly liked Dinah Sheridan, and shook her head at the mention of Joan Collins. Mildred had been friends with Joan's husband Maxwell Reed. If she wasn't in favour of Joan, then she was furious when I mentioned Luise Rainer.

'Oh, Christ! That bitch. Oh, now, she'll ruin the whole darn picture, Orstin. Oh, you've gotta speak to your brother...' She suddenly became agitated. 'Oh, now, wait a minute. Oh, I gotta make a pit stop.' She rushed to the toilet.

With Mildred out of the room, Howard appeared in the doorway. He wondered if Mildred could do it, with a bit of help from me and perhaps Joanna. We were both quiet for a moment as we heard groans coming from the bathroom. Howard crept down the hall and listened, concerned. Silence. I joined him, with Rosebud behind me.

Suddenly the door unlocked and flew open. 'Oh, boys!' she cried, her expression jubilant. 'Oh, boys, do I have good news! The eagle has finally landed.' Howard and I watched as she passed between us, and then fell about laughing so hard so that we could barely stand to laugh any more. Nothing was too much for Mildred.

She called us both. Mildred sat at the head of the

dining table, the light from the standard lamp casting a shadow and therefore disguising her slightly disfigured face. It was with some newfound vigour that she asked us to sit. 'Now, listen to me, Howard.' Her performance was akin to Brando in *The Godfather*. 'When do you want me to start on your picture?'

'It's a photoshoot, Cissie.' Mildred had not heard me. She wiggled off and flopped into the recliner. She asked for her scrapbook and turned to the final few blank pages. I watched her as she held the book to her bosom – she was Hollywood dreaming.

* * *

Right up until the day before the shoot, Mildred consumed only fruit juice and yoghurt for breakfast, and Cuppa-Soup for lunch and dinner. Despite only accepting minuscule portions, and despite instructing that every meal be calorie-counted, Mildred still left half on her plate.

Between meals she took to her exercise bike, determined to appear slimmer on camera than Rita Tushingham. 'She's an elfin type,' said Mildred, who admitted she had not seen Rita onscreen since *Smashing Time* in 1967. She stood before me in the leopard-print leotard. 'I was an elfin type,' she said, pulling off her sweatbands. 'I was Hollywood's Pocket Venus! If that's not the same as 'elfin' then, Christ, what is? Listen, I invented fucking 'elfin'.' She tugged at her fingerless gloves and wobbled towards the make-up room. I took her hand.

'Oh, come on, Cissie.' She was not hearing me. 'It's a photo shoot and it'll be fun.' I let her go.

It was quiet until she reached the mirror in the make-up room. 'I'm the size of an elephant!' she wailed. Mildred probably weighed less than ninety pounds.

* * *

Mildred opted for a black and white dress worn over a pair of 'hold me in pants' that she'd asked me to purchase after seeing a Marks & Spencer advertisement in her newspaper. Over the dress she wore a white jacket with new black patent shoes and a black cocktail hat with a fine black lace veil. The set location would be a redundant shunting yard behind Queenstown Road Station. As she and I, joined by Joanna, exited Kylestrome House, Mildred lifted the veil and added dark shades.

'If anyone asks, tell 'em I'm in character,' she ordered Joanna.

In the two weeks since Howard had asked if she would do him the honour and play the role of Princess Dragomiroff, her left eye had closed almost completely. Her face was melting like ice-cream in August.

It had already been a long morning. Joanna had sat on the edge of the dressing table, helping Mildred with her make-up. Mildred had cried at her own reflection. She'd suggested that I call Peggy Cummins after all to stand in for her. There was no way her fans could see what she'd become. Mildred quoted Mary Pickford, whose niece Gwynne Ruppe had been a friend, saying that she thought it best now to retreat behind closed doors. Joanna quietly suggested that perhaps I really should call Peggy. She was younger and perhaps more able to do it – to make a comeback.

But eventually Mildred snapped to, assuring us that her return to the spotlight would bring joy to the fans. Besides Joanna, Howard, and me, her only other 'fans' were an elderly chap who wrote to her from Abergavenny, a Saudi who sent her chocolates, and Graham, also known as Gilda, a cross-dressing friend of Mr Sherman from St. Mary's.

Howard had secretly explained her condition to the crew in advance, and everyone had prepared.

Unimpressed as we approached the location, Mildred asked the driver if he could find out where her trailer might be. He stopped at a gate and rolled down his window. A man holding a clipboard asked for our names. Mildred shouted over all of us. 'I'm the talent here, my man. Orstin here is my agent and this female is kinda my maid – aren't you, Joanna?'

'Oh, thanks very much, Cissie,' said Joanna. 'You've figured out our roles then!' My stomach clenched with anxiety. Joanna was already pissed off and we hadn't even started yet.

Mildred was immediately taken in by the charms of the photographer Ricardo Alcaide and fell in love with flamboyant stylist Marko Matysik, who in turn fell in love with her. With a new drive, Mildred joined in as they played around: Marko placing gigantic Anouska Hempel hats with metre-long pheasant feathers on her head, and on her feet, four-inch Jimmy Choo heels.

Joanna was joined by Adam's sister Victoria, also on-hand to look after Mildred. Mildred inevitably called for both to take turns escorting her to an outside por-ta-loo. The eagle had not landed for days.

All set for the first scene (wearing a black corset, pencil skirt, giant Hempel hat, Manolo Blahnik heels, furs, and about £750,000 worth of diamonds from Bond Street jewellers) Mildred announced that she needed to visit the powder room. I witnessed Joanna leading Mildred gingerly along a temporary pathway made from scaffolding boards to the loo. 'This is hardly MGM,' I heard Mildred joke loudly as she passed a beefy six-foot-five security guard wearing a black suit, shades, and an earpiece. 'At Metro, the loo would be brought to the star!' I watched as he let both ladies pass before following a few paces behind them. He had not been hired to protect the stars – he was there to guard the thousands of pounds worth of gems borrowed for the shoot, most of which were currently being worn by Mildred.

Joanna waited outside the toilet door. She could hear Mildred talking to herself. After ten minutes Mildred surfaced. The corset was somehow above her midriff, the skirt unfastened and hanging low. Joanna helped Mildred readjust herself. Joanna told me later Mildred asked the security guard if she needed a frisk. Apparently, he only grunted.

It was not until Mildred was almost back on set that she announced she seemed to have lost some of her jewellery. 'Oh, my Gawd,' she said quite matter-of-factly, 'I'm sure I was wearing two diamond earrings.' There was a horrified silence.

Whilst Mildred and Ron Moody calmly drank tea from the catering van, everyone else in the crew

– including Joanna, Victoria, and the security guard – was practically on hands and knees retracing Mildred's footsteps to and from the toilet. I joined Mildred with Ron in the larger of the Pullman cars and asked when she was last aware of having two diamond earrings. She became annoyed as I continued to quiz her.

'Do you know, Mr Moody, my perfectly wonderful Daddy always asked if I needed money, or if I wanted for beautiful fineries. I didn't,' she said, shrugging her shoulders. 'Money dirtied my pocketbook.'

'I'm a Jew,' replied Ron. 'We're supposed to love a bit of the green stuff,' he laughed, passing Mildred a cake plate piled high with cream puffs and horns of plenty.

'Don't suppose you've any of that lovely money now, have you?' she asked. He playfully leant over towards Mildred, wiggling his fingers, his performance every bit as convincing as he had been onscreen as Fagin in *Oliver!* He even broke into an impromptu, *You've Got to Pick a Pocket or Two.* Mildred joined in the chorus despite a mouth full of cream.

Their singing drew the attention of Suna the runner, Marko, and Howard, who had only just arrived, having been with a second stylist borrowing further clothes for the shoot.

Ricardo ended the jubilation with a call to return to set. I passed Victoria, clearly anxious about the earring, coming into the carriage as I left. It was then that there was a second loud voice. To everyone's relief, Victoria had located the Van Cleef & Arpels teardrop diamond earing – but not in the mud. After a fifteen minute search, she'd wondered if somehow Mildred had retained it on her person. Sure enough, after a quick rummage, Mildred retrieved the gem from inside her Wonderbra.

'I had so many of those things once that I guess they don't mean a great deal to me,' she joked as she handed the earring to Victoria, who immediately gave it to the security guard, who was not the least bit amused.

Nor, for that matter, was Suna; the cream cake props for the next scene had disappeared. I suggested Joanna could get some more – she'd hinted she could do with a break. It turned out Suna had spares in the catering truck, only she'd need a moment to spray them with varnish, just as she had the previous assortment. Nobody let on to Mildred and Ron Moody that they'd just eaten horns of plenty coated in Copydex adhesive.

* * *

In the final scene, photographer Ricardo Alcaide gathered Mildred and the rest of the cast and positioned them on the platform beside the train. All eyes were on Mildred: all fifty-four members of the crew, actors, make-up girls, Victoria, Marko, Howard, Suna, four tiny dogs and their handlers, the security guard, Alison Booth, Andi Godfrey, the *Orient Express* staff and me.

Marko stood with his hands clasped together under his chin and whispered to Joanna and me as dry ice billowed around all of us. 'Doesn't she look fabulous?' he sighed. I could almost hear the intake of breath. Mildred and I looked at one another from where I stood just behind Ricardo. I knew by her expression that she was in her element.

'I can work again,' she told me, changed back into her day-clothes. 'I'm going to telephone my agent. I mean honestly, darling, I really could be back there on the screen. It's where I belong, and I don't mean stupid bit-parts in *When Harry Met Sandra*! Shit! What a pile of crap!'

It seemed she'd forgotten for a moment the state of her face. Then she checked her reflection in her Max Factor compact. 'Fuck!' she sighed. 'If I carry on droop-ing I could play Barbara Windsor's mother.'

As we drove away from the shoot, Mildred wound down the window, waving to the crew, and thanking Marko and Ricardo deeply. As the car pulled away she shouted, 'I'm ready when you are, Mr DeMille!'

She never saw the photos in print.

* * *

Having asked Ricardo to mail some test shots to June Epstein, Mildred spent the next four days waiting for the phone to ring. On Wednesday, the day after the shoot, she was sure June would call with one or two ideas for new roles. By Thursday, having decided she'd have to call herself, Mildred was positive something would come by the weekend. The silence was deafening. She spent the weekend in bed. The pain of rejection was harder to bear than her illness.

It was only when I received a text from Richard Shel-ton with details of The Rat Pack concert that he was giving at Canary Wharf that Mildred showed any sign of getting up at all.

Mildred and Richard had hit it off well on the *Orient Express* shoot. After he gave her an impromptu teaser, she deemed him the very best Sinatra she'd heard since she'd hung out with Ol' Blue Eyes himself. That said, she admitted to Richard as we all waited between takes that he'd done nothing for her when she'd first seen him perform. 'Then I saw him perform in another way,' she laughed.

Home by four on the evening of the concert, I found Mildred in the make-up room. She told me she'd been weeping for hours. 'Oh, Orstin,' she cried, 'vanity got me in the end.' The left side of her face seemed to have slipped further. What impressed me the most was the fact that she still cared enough to bother with the full make-up routine nonetheless.

Soothing her, I helped her put the finishing touches to her outfit: canary-yellow suit, straw hat with osprey feathers, and mink wrap.

The buzzer went at half past five; we were in the car provided by Richard and on our way to Canary Wharf minutes later. The traffic being heavy, the driver skirted around the edge of the city. Throughout the journey, I pointed out London landmarks in the distance. For once she was quiet, then nodded off.

I'd called Adam and Lee the previous night. They'd recently moved to the area and I hoped they'd fancy joining us. Both were waiting by the edge of the stage as we approached. Mildred appeared happy to see them but tired from the journey. It was a battle to get through the crowds to the VIP area, but once there we were soon greeted by a bouncy Richard, thrilled she'd made it. As he got on one knee and kissed her hand, all eyes were suddenly on her.

The atmosphere was brilliant. Richard belted out *I've Got You Under My Skin* before pausing to tell the audience how proud and honoured he was to be performing tonight in the presence of a movie star from Hollywood's Golden Age – who knew 'the man and his music'. I felt a lump in my throat as I helped Mildred to her feet. She was acknowledging with renewed energy the round of applause and loud whoops from the crowd. Richard dedicated his next song, *The Way You Look Tonight*, to her.

It was during the interval that Richard came looking for us, bringing Sammy Davis Jr. with him. She threw her arms around Richard. 'Oh, darling, thank you for doing that for me,' she said. 'You have no idea how much it means to me at this moment.'

Richard pulled a photographer over. I sensed her unease at being photographed, something she'd never have shied away from before then. She asked that he take her good side. She shielded her deformity with dark glasses. She then posed with fans and signed autographs. I looked at my watch when we were back in the car – a quarter to eleven. She slept all the way home.

The following week, Adam called Mildred to tell her she'd made it onto the front page of a local Canary Wharf newspaper. Mildred told Zsa Zsa Gabor's daughter Francesca Hilton to inform 'Mother' that she was in the *London Times* – the headline read 'I Was Attacked by Errol Flynn!'

Sixteen

The Wedding

I t had rained every day for a week, but I was hoping for sunshine the next day. I'd left London four days ago for the Forest of Dean. Mildred had been in the hospital for a week before I left.

I was outside the front of the Speech House, an unmissable edifice originally built as a hunting lodge for King Charles II in 1669, where, according to Joanna's grandfather Roy, a Verderers' Court was created for the protection of the King's greenery and deer.

I could make out a herd of perhaps eight small deer on the other side of the road, hidden mostly by bracken; their saucer-like eyes watched me watching them. And sheep, lots of sheep.

Joanna was inside. She said I should call her when I saw Corinne's car. It was damp and humid. Joanna despised the damp; she complained it turned her hair frizzy. However, having been in London for so many years, she was happy to be home, frizzy hair and all. Joanna's family were especially delighted that she had settled into teaching in Chepstow, about twenty miles from the Speech House.

She and I had gone out the night before, just the two of us. We became sentimental and reminisced about where we had first met: Brats, a small gift shop on the Fulham Road. It was her first week there, picking up a few shifts in between her studies, and my last before heading off for a new career as a restaurant manager.

Joanna asked what my initial thoughts of her had been. Having consumed two beers and a bottle of wine, and about to open the second on an empty stomach, I said that on first setting eyes on Joanna I thought that her clothes were too tight – the alcohol apparently turned me brutally honest. Joanna playfully slapped me and said she thought I looked like Screech from the TV show *Saved by the Bell* with my wiry hair and goatee. We were a perfect match.

We laughed until our stomachs ached over the fun times we had had, firstly at her tumble-down student house in Sheen, Richmond, and then in Islington, the flat so cold that we had had to cuddle around the gas cooker to warm ourselves up on winter mornings. We spoke about all the characters we had met along the way, friends and family. Joanna regretted never having met my grandmother, Violet. I joked with her that it wouldn't have been a meeting but an interview, with Violet carefully assessing whether Joanna was good enough for her grandson.

Our conversation inevitably turned to Mildred. There was no doubting our love for her. Joanna mimicked the line 'We're family', coined by Barbara Windsor and copied by Mildred. She raised her glass. 'To Cissie!' she said. We chinked glasses: 'To family!'

* * *

The Forest was beautiful. It was the second of September, a perfect late summer day. Joanna and I were to be married the next day. My stomach churned over (no thanks to the large amount of alcohol the prior night) thinking about it. Family and friends from every imaginable part of our lives were all descending en masse.

My parents had been two of the first to arrive yesterday afternoon. Dad couldn't bear the thought of the long drive to Gloucestershire from Worthing, so my brother-in-law Barry had volunteered to be the designated driver.

My pregnant sister Rowena waxed lyrical as she told me of the lovely scenery they'd passed on the way. Neat little stone cottages with roses around the door and picket fences. Rowena romanticised living in the country, batch baking for the Women's Institute with a huge Aga.

Mother, on the other hand, had apparently been grumbling about the unimaginable distance. According to Rowena, she'd retorted that she would not like to live in the country, suggesting that given the choice she'd 'rather live on a roundabout'. Her tone, according to Rowena, had been most imperious.

Once they'd arrived and Joanna and I had had tea with Mother in the small lounge, simply decorated with tapestries and mismatched oak occasional tables, Mother admitted that the hotel, at least, was most to her liking. She added that she'd have favoured the setting even more had the Speech House been closer to home.

Chatty Uncle Paul and Aunt Barbara had arrived early that morning from East Grinstead with my cousins and their partners, followed by my Godparents and other relatives. The family all hit it off rather quickly with a writer friend of mine, Michael Collins, and also with Nicola and Bertie. Chums Lesley and Adrian joined them at the Verderers' Court for a hearty breakfast.

The amalgamation of relatives and friends, including a merry group from my art school days in Epsom, made for something of a large walking party. I counted fifteen or more as they filed past me and stood on the steps of the hotel, planning a meander through the forest.

Michael and Nicola were the least dressed for the occasion: he in wide-legged flannels and spats, she in perilously high heels. I watched them all disappear through the trees, but could still hear Michael's laugh. I laughed too and wished I were with them: a guest and not a main player at this wedding.

Just as I was about to go back inside, Corinne tore up behind the wheel of her black VW Golf convertible, with Howard beside her and Mildred buckled up in the back, all with their shades on and the sunroof down. She came to a thunderous stop in front of me.

Having been exposed to the elements, Mildred's hair was Phyllis Diller wild. Her outfit, a blue naval blazer with *Dynasty*-esque shoulder pads, white blouse, and a red scarf tied at the neck, gave every impression of an Air France stewardess.

Despite her amusing get-up, up close there was no denying that she looked like a sick woman. In the few days since I'd last seen her, Mildred's face had somehow sagged even further – her left eye was now permanently closed and her jaw slightly out of kilter. Ever the trooper, she still wore (courtesy of Howard's steady hand) false eye-lashes and lashings of lipstick. Howard had been staying at the flat. He looked exhausted.

'We made it,' said Mildred triumphantly, as I flipped the passenger seat forward to help her from the back of the car. Wobbly, but standing on terra firma, she hugged me.

Also awaiting their arrival was Joanna. She joined me on the gravel drive. Behind her was Moira Gould, the hotel manager, and receptionists Claire and Kerenza. Despite my briefing them on Mildred's condition, I was concerned that they would not be prepared. How I misjudged them; the staff couldn't have been more charming.

It was Joanna who was the most alarmed; she was simply unable to mask her shock at Mildred's deterioration.

Mildred, seemingly unable to retain saliva, had soiled the front of her blouse. The drool spread like ink on blotting paper, stained scarlet by the lipstick she had been constantly re-applying. It gave the impression that she'd been bleeding from the mouth. Joanna embraced her. As she pulled away, she manoeuvred Mildred's scarf to hide the stain.

'Oh, Cissie,' Joanna said, biting her lip, 'I'm so pleased you've come.'

'Oh, darling girl,' said Mildred weepily, 'I wouldn't have missed it for the world.'

'I'm so excited to meet you, Mildred,' said Claire, defusing the situation. She had known Joanna since their teenage years at the local secondary school. Claire motioned for me to comfort Joanna as Claire took Mildred's hands in hers. 'I've heard so much about you,' she enthused. 'I'm so bloody excited. We've only ever had Chris Tarrant stay here – never a Hollywood movie star, mind.'

'Oh, darling girl,' spluttered Mildred. 'I'd be excited to meet me too.'

Claire hugged Joanna and then me. 'We'll look after her,' she said to Joanna, who beamed back at her old friend.

Moira took control. Leading Mildred to the front door, I heard her tell Mildred how honoured they were to have her as a guest. Kerenza and Claire helped Howard with Mildred's luggage: two large suitcases, a Peter Jones hatbox, her Max Factor make-up case, leatherette jewel case, suit carrier, a flowered hold-all, mink coat, and sable wrap.

'Bloody hell,' laughed Claire, two bags in each hand. 'She certainly travels like a movie star!'

'She's not grumbled once,' said Corinne. 'I was going at some speed back there and she never complained – I think she loved every minute of it.'

'She called us 'Thelma, Louise, and Man',' said Howard as he hugged Joanna.

By looking at him, I knew it hadn't been easy since I'd left London. He'd practically camped out at Chelsea and Westminster Hospital. It was touch and go as to whether she'd be released in time for our wedding at all. In the end, a specialist had informed Howard only yesterday that he was happy to let her go. I'd stupidly assumed this meant she was getting better. Now,

Howard's face told me otherwise. He watched Moira take Mildred into the hotel and then turned to me. Suddenly his eyes teared up.

I mouthed, 'How is it?'

He could only shake his head.

'How long?' I asked him. He didn't need to say another word. He never did.

Mother said that from the moment we had been able to communicate, he and I had had a special bond. We had our own language, or so she would say. Apparently nobody else could decode it – she referred to it as our 'twin-thing'.

There were no words necessary now. Howard eventually managed to choke out 'brain tumour', but his look had already told me all I needed to know. My heart flickered. I just hoped Mildred would make it through the weekend.

* * *

Moira appeared in the bar. Mildred was fine, but had taken to her bed for a rest. Moira handed Howard a room key in one hand and a brandy in the other. She had placed him in the room next to Mildred's. Howard knocked the drink back with one gulp.

He told me that Mildred had requested a 'pit-stop' just as they were driving past Gloucester City, towards the Forest of Dean. Corinne had pulled into the carpark of a pub.

'The scene inside was biblical,' said Corinne, sitting on a bar stool, drinking from a glass of champagne Moira had just passed to her. 'As we arrived, punters in the pub just stared at her. Like Moses parting the Red Sea, Mildred's presence alone moved swathes of customers to allow Howard on one side and me on the other to manoeuvre Mildred through the bar to the restroom! I tell you, it's not an overstatement, it truly was biblical!'

Howard's face told a sadder story. He added that there had been a boy of about eight years old, seated with his parents and younger siblings close to the doors to the restrooms. The boy was staring and pointing and then, as Mildred approached, asked in a very loud voice, 'What is wrong with that lady's face? Why is she so ugly?'

Although the outburst was purely innocent, Howard felt Mildred must have heard. He told us how he felt her grip on his arm tighten as the boy repeated and repeated his words, his father trying his best to shut him up. Howard said that at that moment, due to the boy's raised voice, all eyes were on Mildred. He felt her anguish; for the first time in her life, Mildred didn't want to be ogled.

'But she's made it here now,' said Moira.

She refilled Howard's glass, reassuring us that Mildred was quite comfortable. Moira had asked a chambermaid by the name of Crystal to 'unpack her'.

'She's quite taken with Crystal,' said Moira as she joined us for a glass of champagne. 'From what I can tell, Mildred seems to have known a Crystal once.'

'That'll be Joan Crawford,' Howard said, his tone happier. 'Joan Crawford played Crystal Allen in *The Women* in 1939 – Mildred was cast as her French maid Hélène.'

'Well, it's beyond comical,' laughed Moira. 'Crystal can't even understand her, yet somehow they're getting along like a couple of teenagers.'

'Mildred sharing a laugh and a joke with a girl? Well, that's a first,' I said to myself.

Obeying tradition, Joanna reluctantly left the hotel to stay with her parents, leaving me to host a dinner for the guests who had already arrived. By half-past six, there were around twenty-five family members and friends in the bar; Joanna's younger brother Jonny and his boyfriend Justin being the latest additions.

Mildred arrived just as we were about to take our seats in the dining room. Unbeknown to me, Howard and Crystal had been her dressers. Mildred was wearing her orange, emerald, and calamine-pink Pucci dress with woollen tights and strappy sandals. Her hair had been tamed underneath a colourful sequined hat with a feathered bird of paradise detail. She'd decided to go the whole hog with the jewellery; her hand was every bit as sparkly as Liberace (whom, needless to say, Mildred had known).

Mother took Mildred's arm and gingerly placed Mildred on a chair directly beside hers – I placed myself on the other side of Mildred. Alarmed by Mildred's appearance, Mother played nurse. She asked a waiter for a straw and helped Mildred drink champagne from a tall highball. 'Oh, my dear Pamela,' said Mildred, letting Mother hold a napkin to her chin. She waved the glass away after struggling with the drink. 'The darndest thing happened: I'm certain I've caught Bell's palsy whilst I've been ill at the hospital.'

Mother sympathised.

Mildred watched Howard at the other end of the table. She tugged at my shirt. She felt Howard and Corinne should 'shack up'. She reminded me she'd known Corinne's family, the Copes, in Hollywood and they seemed to have a 'bit of moolah'. She apparently assumed that Howard would be interested in a woman if she only had enough money.

* * *

I was awoken by the ringing of the phone next to my bed. I grabbed my watch: seven o'clock. I answered it.

The voice was Kerenza's. Mildred had rung reception and was asking for me.

'She sounds like it's urgent,' said Kerenza, worried.

I pulled on yesterday's T-shirt and shorts and dashed from my room to Mildred's – the door was ajar, the bed empty. I heard her in the bathroom. She was distressed.

'Oh, Orstin, darling!' she said, spotting me. 'The most dreadful thing just occurred to me.'

'Are you sick?' I asked unthinkingly – then I realised that of course she was. She quivered as she headed to the bed. I helped her to sit. As her distress slowly subsided, the calamity was revealed: who would do her hair?

It was Joanna's mother Julie who came up with the solution: Steve's Hairdressing Salon in the nearby village of Rustbridge. Julie promised to call back once she'd made the appointment – luckily Steve's opened early. Kerenza brought Mildred a breakfast of toast and coffee whilst I went back to my room to shower.

Mildred was in the reception area by the time I come down from my room. Despite the warmth of the day, Mildred was wearing her mink over a candy-pink tracksuit Joanna had bought her from New Look, with dark glasses and her 'Satisfaction Guaranteed' baseball cap. I argued that the fine weather hardly called for a fur coat, but Mildred thought otherwise.

'Orstin, darling, the kids who work here are starstruck!' she whispered loudly. I spied Kerenza giggling; she'd obviously overheard. 'They're country people, darling – these kids want Hollywood and I'm giving it to 'em!'

Unbeknown to Mildred, Julie had warned Steve, the proprietor of the salon, of Mildred's fragile health and worrying appearance.

Steve was prepared. The salon, a York-stone single-storey building with a lilac interior, was the sort one saw on high streets during the seventies, with customers sitting under space-age hairdryers. Steve was standing on the threshold, awaiting our arrival.

'Miss Shay, I presume,' said Steve as he took her hand. 'I knew it had to be you, flower. I've been fighting off the paparazzi, mind,' he laughed. 'There've been hordes of them outside here, there has!'

'Oh, darling,' said Mildred, allowing him to lead her inside.

I watched from the cash desk as Steve and his chief hairstylist Clare sat her in front of a mirror.

'Come on then, my lover,' said Steve in his rich Forest accent, teasing her hair with a comb, 'how many of them Oscar statuettes has you at home?'

Mildred was eating up the attention. I left them to it. Clare called me two hours later. Mildred was ready.

I parked up outside. I spied only her new honey-blonde hairdo through the window – she was otherwise surrounded by people. An old-fashioned door-bell rang as I entered. Mildred's voice was loud amongst a bevy of elderly ladies, Steve, Clare, and two younger hairdressers. Steve walked over to greet me. Mildred was unaware I was there. She was signing autographs.

'She's incredible,' he said. 'I tell you what, them young movie stars, they've not got a patch on Mildred Shay, mind! Her stories – marvellous they are, marvellous.'

A large elderly woman sitting on a chair directly by the door watched me. I smiled; she did not. She had her hair pinned up and was wearing a pastel hairdresser's cape around her shoulders. It turned out that Mrs Frieda Burns, a neighbour of Joanna's gran Betty, and Steve's regular, was not very impressed by the hoopla surrounding Mildred.

'She a friend of yours?' barked Frieda Burns, nodding in Mildred's direction. Mildred was still in full throttle.

'Yes, she is,' I replied cheerily. 'Her name is Mildred, Mildred Shay, she worked in Hollywood…'

Frieda Burns cut me off. 'Oh, I know all that,' she griped. 'All that braggin'!' She looked over to Mildred again. 'And they've all been lapping it up, mind.'

'Come on, Mrs Burns, we don't get celebrities here all that often, mind,' said Steve as he overheard her grumbling.

'Yes, we have,' said Mrs Burns firmly. 'We've had that exercise lady that used to jig about on the box in the mornings. Hers was called Mad summat?'

'Oh, yes, you're right, Mrs Burns – 'Mad' Lizzie Webb, she switched on the Christmas lights someplace,' said Steve, rubbing his chin. 'I'd forgotten all about her, look.'

'And my late husband Dennis, he saw The Krankies at the Clauseway Club, mind.' She suddenly looked puzzled. 'At least, I think it were The Krankies, that wee Scottish lad and his dad, that be saying 'Fan Dabi Dozi' to the kiddies.'

'Oh, yes, The Krankies, forgotten about them too, Mrs Burns,' said Steve, waiting for Mildred to finish signing an autograph for Mrs Sylvia Lucas. 'And now we've had Mildred Shay from Hollywood come visit,' he added.

Mildred spied me and waved. Steve went over to her and helped Mildred with her fur coat.

Frieda Burns was still sitting fiddling with her curlers by the time Mildred was finally ready to leave. She watched her every move with a critical eye.

'I tell you what,' said Frieda Burns to Sylvia Lucas. 'She's bloody trooper, I'll give 'er that, mind. If I looked the way hers be looking, mind, I'd be indoors and never come out again, look!'

'Miss Shay,' said Steve, 'it's been an honour. You're welcome back any time.'

* * *

Back at the hotel, Mildred said she needed to take a rest. I took her to her room. On a hanger on the outside of the wardrobe door was the chosen outfit for our wedding: the short canary-yellow skirt and matching jacket.

A fortnight prior in London, Joanna had spent an afternoon with Mildred, selecting the best possible outfit to wear to the wedding. To complement Joanna's grandmother Betty and Betty's many sisters, Joanna had selected a pastel floral dress to be worn with a pale pink jacket and feathered hat in soft pinks and oranges.

However, when it came to packing, Mildred asked Howard to put the floral number back in the wardrobe. According to Mildred, Clark Gable always said, 'Mildred Shay's legs are the best in town.' She lived by his compliment, and so it was that, almost seven decades on, she explicitly asked that the yellow mini-skirt be placed in the suitcase.

'They'll not look at me twice if I'm trussed up like the Queen Mother, for Christ's sake,' Mildred had said as she held the yellow skirt to herself during the afternoon spent packing.

At ninety-three, Mildred still thought she could pull.

Mother volunteered to assist Mildred in getting ready for the church service. She told me later that she had been rather shocked to see Mildred in her underwear: a silver jewelled thong and a rather gloomy grey Wonderbra, both a gift from Baby. The bra was at least two sizes too big.

'It was a revelation, darling,' said Mother later.

I could hear Aunt Barbara in conversation with friends of Joanna's parents. They and the rest of the congregation were on the terrace of the Speech House, sipping champagne and tucking into canapés after the church service nearby. Apparently, two things from the service would stay with Aunt Barbara: firstly the exquisite operatic singing voice of our friend Ingrid, and secondly 'that movie star's whistling hearing aids'.

Jo's dad Kenneth located a chair and footrest for Mildred. Shortly afterwards, I noticed she'd nodded off, her mouth wide open, saliva trickling down her chin. Moira noticed too. She and Howard took Mildred to her room.

Mildred returned an hour later for the wedding breakfast, but then retreated to her room again after Howard's long best man speech and Ken's whistle-stop tour of praise for his daughter. Mother and Corinne helped Mildred undress and put her to bed.

Mildred reminisced about her own three weddings: each one a rather rushed affair and nothing like as romantic as today's setting. Corinne switched the television on for Mildred. Just as they were about to leave, Mildred remembered she needed to take her pills, pointing to dozens of tablets of varying shapes and sizes in bottles on her dressing table. Not waiting for Mother to fetch a glass of water, Mildred swallowed three at a time, washed down with a slug of champagne. She was flat out in less than five minutes.

Sometime later, Moira located Howard on the patio. It transpired Mildred had woken up to find it was dark outside; moreover, she could hear music and had rung reception, asking the staff to find me. Knowing I was with our guests, Moira had said she'd alert Howard. I noticed he had been gone for some time and asked

Rowena if she'd seen him. She'd seen Howard go to Mildred's room.

It was just as Joanna and I were about to have the first dance that Mildred appeared on Howard's arm. Gone was the yellow two-piece; in its place the Eric Way evening gown and a long flowing sable cape. Mildred remained on the dance floor for most of the evening, or chatted with receptionist Claire and her husband Adam. I watched Mildred with Claire and a group of Joanna's girlfriends on the dancefloor as the band played a rendition of Beyoncé's *Crazy in Love*.

Tired, Mildred asked a guest to help her to the quiet of the lounge. Joanna found her seated alone by the fire, her eyes closed. Mildred wanted to go to bed. Joanna helped her.

Joanna, still in her wedding gown, undressed Mildred. She helped remove Mildred's make-up and moisturised her face and her hands. She hung Mildred's dress and fur in the wardrobe and helped her drink from a glass of water as best she could without a straw, before tucking her into bed.

Unable to locate Joanna for half an hour, I decided to go and look for her. It was Adrian who told me he'd seen her with Mildred in the lounge. Kerenza on the desk had seen the two of them head to Mildred's room.

I found Joanna closing the door to Mildred's room. Slightly inebriated, I told her that her mum or mine could have done all that. I protested that this was our night and we had so little of it left. She put her finger to my lips.

'Shh, Austin. I wanted to spend time with Cissie.

She's my friend too.' She took my hand and we both peered into Mildred's room – she was snoring. 'She said I'm the only girlfriend she ever had.'

I thought back to Mildred's stories of jealous women, of Honeychilde Wilder and Arline Judge, of how they'd abandoned her on one of the darkest days of her life to go to a party. Joanna interrupted my thoughts with the sound of Mildred's door closing. She kissed me.

The party was almost over.

Seventeen

The Birthday Party

Our honeymoon was just a short two-night stay in a smart hotel close to Bristol, then onto Joanna's – now our – cottage, our new home together. With Joanna's new school term about to begin, I decided to return to my pied-à-terre, as we now jokingly referred to the flat.

I took the National Express from Chepstow to Victoria, then walked to the flat to drop off my bags. The flat was silent, tidy, and untouched, aside from the tell-tale sign of Lady Janet having been in to feed Rosebud. Standing in the doorway to the living room, I already missed the roar of the television and the sickly smell of Giorgio Beverly Hills perfume. The kitchen was neat too, devoid of Mildred's smalls floating in the sink.

The doctors insisted Mildred stay put at the hospital so they could ensure she'd be comfortable. It had been two weeks since they'd diagnosed Mildred with a brain tumour, and no time at all since our wedding. Howard and I begged the doctors not to reveal the prognosis to Mildred. Rightly or wrongly, I wanted Mildred to enjoy the time she had left, rather than pine away in her recliner – her dancing at the wedding proved my theory right.

I arrived at the hospital to find Mildred make-up free, sitting in a chair next to her bed in a leisure suit, over which she wore the pale blue dressing gown with the faux fur cuffs.

'Oh, Orstin,' she mumbled, holding a handkerchief to her mouth. 'I look awful.'

I gave her a kiss and pulled up a chair so I was directly opposite her. She was not looking at me, but around me. I followed her gaze towards a young woman in a zip-up jumpsuit. Mildred lowered her voice.

'See that broad, Orstin,' she said. 'The dame behind you. Oh, my, she's real sick, she's an anorexic.' I looked over my shoulder. The painfully thin woman was lying on her bed reading a copy of *Marie Claire*. 'I've been chatting with her and I've told her she's just gotta eat. She's nodding, but honestly, it's not going in.' The girl looked up from her magazine, her face skeletal. 'I told her I was in Hollywood, I told her that the gals hardly ate much at all at the studios, but we didn't make ourselves look starved, for Christ's sake – we would never have got a part if we had done that, nor a man for that matter.'

I sensed the woman could hear Mildred and was becoming twitchy; I did my best to change the subject. Mildred asked me to open the small cupboard next to her bed. Inside were a few clothes; everything else that she had had with her in Gloucestershire for the wedding Howard had unpacked and left at the flat.

She asked me to pull out two envelopes tucked beside her shrimp-coloured cardigan. Inside the larger envelope was a card and a drawing dedicated to 'Great

Aunty Mildred' from Minnie and Ben. She asked me to pass it to her. She kissed it and then handed it back to me, asking that I stand it on her bedside table.

Mildred had had very few visitors since returning to hospital: some old friends from St. Mary's Church, her former priest, old friends Kiki, Rosemary, Timothy, and the Hendersons, who'd moved in recent times to East Sussex. To my surprise and delight, Mildred told me Resheda had popped in. Obviously learning from Social Services that Mildred was at the hospital, she'd brought as a gift a bag of homemade Persian chickpea biscuits. Mildred had them in a paper bag next to a jug of water. 'Orstin, take them home. I tell you, Re-shit-a's cookies, they've given me the most awful gas.'

Mildred's attention was drawn back to the woman opposite. 'Second thoughts: leave them here. I'll try and feed them to that poor creature.' She nodded her head to Meghan, who had put her earphones in.

I left Mildred just before eight as she sat on Meghan's bed with her tiny arm around her.

* * *

The next evening, I returned to Chelsea and Westminster with half a dozen fan letters. I'd seen Calum the postman outside Mildred's block that morning. He'd asked after her and then proceeded to hand me a small stack of mail: three circulars, a card, and several handwritten letters, all with U.S. stamps.

To my amazement, I later discovered that Mildred's address had somehow made it onto a 'fan mail website' based in America. I vaguely remembered she had received a fan letter after the newspaper interview and had replied to it – did her correspondent put her details online? Seven of the twelve letters came from correction centres; another from Texas State Penitentiary. A chap by the name of Charles, living in Germany, wrote to say he'd seen everything Mildred had ever done, whereas a Welshman in Swansea by the name of Robert Vaughn Jones begged for a signed photo, adding that he'd not know quite what to do with himself if she failed to answer.

When I arrived, Mildred was sitting in the chair next to her bed, dressed in hospital nightclothes, over which she wore her dressing gown with a flowery scarf tied around her head. She was talking at Meghan across the width of the ward. I heard her ask if Meghan had eaten any supper. Meghan didn't respond. Unbeknown to Mildred, she had plugged into her earphones again. Mildred was thrilled to see me.

'Oh, darling, that poor creature, she has everything to live for – I met her mother today, I tell you, the family has a ton of money...' I interrupted her by scattering the fan letters on her bed. With only one eye operational, Mildred couldn't make out what they were at first. I took one and opened it and proceeded to read aloud.

Dear Miss Shay,

I've seen all your films; I think you are beautiful and talented. We have film night at the prison weekly and I always ask for one of your pictures...'

And so it went on.

For once, Mildred was dumbfounded. She took the letter from me. I picked up another letter.

Dear Mildred Shay,

I hope this finds you in good spirits. I saw you last night in The Women, *I feel you stole every scene away from Miss Joan Crawford and Miss Rosalind Russell...*

Mildred took this letter also. Still completely mystified, she held it right up to her one eye and stared.

'What is this, Orstin? Is this a hoax? Am I on *Candid Camera?*' she asked, holding the letters out to me in astonishment.

'No, Cissie,' I said, beaming. 'Mildred, you have fan mail.'

She somehow managed to get to her feet and gathered all the letters and held them to her bosom. 'Oh, how would you like that?' she said. 'People like me!'

A German lady who had arrived shortly after Mildred tutted and then groaned so loudly it all but ricocheted around the ward. Mildred gave her daggers.

'Oh, Orstin, darling,' she said, 'that broad is jealous that I'm somebody. The nice doctor came to see me and I asked him if he happened to know Mildred Shay.'

'Did he?' I asked.

'He didn't say. Now, read me some more of my fan mail, will you, dear? And make sure you enunciate – remember I'm deaf, for Christ's sake!' she said as she stuck her tongue out at her room-mate, who was fortunately otherwise occupied with the *People's Friend*.

'I tell you, Orstin, I haven't been in a dorm like this since Bob Considine got me involved with the USO – living box and cox with Pat Kirkwood as we toured army camps during the war!'

The next night I brought with me four more letters that had been lying on the doormat when I got in from work; the night after that, Larry stopped me with a parcel as I was entering Kylestrome House. The sender was a Mr Chuck James from New Zealand who, it transpired, had sent a book. A pictorial on the history of Metro-Goldwyn-Mayer, it was already autographed by June Allyson, Esther Williams, Virginia Parsons, Shirley Chambers, Ruth Hussey, Joan Fontaine and Anita Page. The fan included a crisp £50 note to cover the return postage and a box of Swiss chocolates. On opening the envelope, Mildred dove straight in and devoured the delicately-wrapped candy.

'Orstin,' she said, holding up the note while dribbling creamy fondant, 'do you think he'll expect the change?'

Mildred made me read the first batch of letters out again just to make a point.

* * *

When I arrived on Saturday morning, Mildred was not in her bed. I wondered whether she'd decided to visit the small TV room for a look at James Martin on *Saturday Kitchen*.

I was met in the corridor by a specialist who told

me Mildred had been extremely aggressive, almost violent, with another patient that morning. Mildred had attacked the German lady – a Mrs Weber – believing she'd stolen some of Mildred's fan mail, and then, during lunch, had clashed with Meghan. I cringed thinking about what Mildred might have said.

The specialist added that Mildred had also been anxious most days, and was growing worse. Since the wedding, Mildred had been asking for her daughter. I promised to see what I could do.

When Mildred did appear, she was in a wheelchair with her powder-blue dressing gown around her shoulders. Watching Meghan's fretful reaction to Mildred's return, I suggested a change of scenery. I took Mildred in her wheelchair to the lift and then to a small café on the ground floor.

I pulled her up to a table, and suddenly noticed she was crying silently. I couldn't make out whether her tears were for sadness or for joy. I asked her about Meghan. Mildred had no idea what I was talking about; however, she did recall her argument with Mrs Weber – although she had somehow confused Mrs Weber with her upstairs neighbour Inga Schmidt.

'Oh, well, that old bitch has been complaining about me to the Duke of Westminster,' she said angrily. 'I tell you, I've heard her inside my television set, and she's intercepted the phone line, too.'

I calmed Mildred by taking her tiny hand, naked of nail varnish and jewellery besides her wedding ring. I changed the subject. I told her that Ben and Minnie had been asking after her.

'Oh, that little boy,' she said peacefully. 'Why, he's as cute as a bug's ear – I should speak to my agent, he could be in pictures.'

I ordered us a coffee each. Mildred's was served to her in a sippy cup. She was suddenly too animated to drink.

She told me that that morning, as she woke, there had been a boy standing next to her bed. 'He was in his short pants. He held my hand, and his smile! Oh, his big smile,' she said, in almost a dreamlike state.

'Who, Mildred?' I asked. 'Are you thinking about Ben?'

'The child, that beautiful child!' she said, suddenly sobbing.

'He made you a card,' I said, reassuring her. 'Ben and Minnie, you've got the card next to your bed.'

Mildred became anxious, annoyed that I did not understand her. She dried her eyes with a tissue from her pocket.

'Oh, for Christ's sake,' she said. Her outburst attracted the attention of fellow customers. I held and massaged her hand. Suddenly calmer, she fumbled with her tissue, wiping liquid from her mouth. 'Oh, Orstin, I'm talking about my baby brother Arnold!' With that, she began to yowl.

My entire body went cold. I got up from my chair and crouched at her feet. Mildred's head flopped on my shoulder. She whispered in my ear, 'Wouldn't you like to meet him, Orstin? Let's go back to my bedroom and see if he's still here.'

Before I could process what she was saying, Mildred began to cough. The cough was so vigorous that it shook her frail body. She retched and burped. A petite lady in a blue uniform appeared, offering assistance. I was thrilled to see it was Nelly-Lyn.

'Hello, beautiful lady,' she said as she knelt before Mildred. 'Oh, my, you do look lovely in that colour dressing gown, miss.'

Nelly-Lyn had to remind Mildred that she'd visited her at the flat. Mildred was polite enough and smiled as best she could, but seemed completely unaware of who Nelly-Lyn was. When Nelly-Lyn left, Mildred asked me why Toshia Mori was at the hospital. She presumed it was because her old Japanese-born Hollywood friend was on the same film set as she was. Mildred looked about her.

'Do you suppose Cukor will tell me when I'm due on set?' she asked me, befuddled. 'Tell me, why is that Nelly-Lyn female working on the picture? She's playing my maid, I suppose?'

Mildred pulled from her dressing gown pocket a lipstick. She applied it so blindly, so wildly, that she looked clown-like. With her appearance drawing stares from fellow patients and visitors, I felt I should wheel her back to the ward. But she wanted to stay.

Since her mood seemed steadier, I quizzed her more on Arnold, trying to ascertain how rational she was.

'Arnold?' she said quizzically, grasping for her sippy-cup. 'Arnold's dead, Orstin. I told you, my darling brother was killed by a drunken chauffeur in front of my mother and my beloved grandmother...' Her voice trailed off as she grew distressed once more.

'Why are you asking me about Arnold? Why Arnold?' she asked anxiously.

A nurse who'd been queuing for a coffee asked me to stand aside and managed to settle her. I followed him as he wheeled Mildred back to the ward. The specialist had warned Howard the day he collected her for the journey to Gloucestershire that the tumour could start to make her moods quite erratic. All she could ask me now was to fetch Baby, over and over.

'Orstin, Mama wants her Baby-girl, why won't you bring Mama's Baby-girl?' she begged.

I was asked to wait outside as the nurse helped Mildred into bed. Given the go-ahead, I returned to her bedside to bid her goodnight. She pleaded that I ring Baby. I took her hand and promised to ring her again that night.

As I left she sighed loudly, 'Goodnight, Arnold.'

Somehow, thinking back to our chat on the edge of her bed last Thanksgiving, I found her words comforting.

* * *

I was awoken the next morning by the phone ringing. It was just before eight. The caller was a nurse from Chelsea and Westminster. She handed the phone to Mildred.

Mildred told me she had to check herself out of the hospital; she had to make the trip to the US to see Baby. She called it 'mother's intuition'; she felt in her bones that Baby needed her Mama. She needed me to book flights, look into travel insurance – she needed me to pack! Mildred decided we should leave after her ninety-fourth birthday.

'Ninety-four, fuck!' she laughed.

She rang off before I had the chance to say I would need to speak to my boss, who had recently been lenient in allowing me time away from my desk (albeit unpaid) as I went to and from the hospital. I'd need to speak to Joanna as well. One thing was clear: Mildred, as frail as she was, was on a mission.

When I arrived at Chelsea and Westminster just over an hour later, Mildred was sitting beside her bed in her pale pink leisure suit. It was covered in lipstick and stained with nail varnish.

'Darling, I've never learnt how to pack or unpack, so I need you to help me now,' she said, pointing at a jumble of clothes on the bed and tumbling out of her locker. On top of the mountain was a jotter pad on which, in a spidery hand, she had written a long list of instructions.

'Listen, when we get to Hollywood I can feed Baby's animals, clean out the parrot and all the birds, and put Gordon in his place and remind that man whose house he is living in.'

'It's not that easy, Cissie,' I said, trying to smother my annoyance that she felt I was able to drop everything at any moment.

Mildred appeared to have selective hearing. She talked over me, ordering me to start packing her luggage as the hospital was bound to need the bed for some 'hopeless cripple'. I left her to find a nurse who assured me there was no way she would be released that day. I calmed Mildred's nerves by telling her the doctors were making checks to see how well she'd respond to travel.

'For Christ's sake, Orstin, it's Baby who should be

checked over – I think she needs a new hip. Oh, fuck, I've gotta get to Baby!' she yelped.

* * *

By eight on Monday morning I was standing before Mildred again in the Adele Dixon ward. She'd deteriorated significantly in just a few hours. The determination that had been there yesterday seemed to have gone. It obviously pained her to speak; she was holding the left side of her face as if to support it from sliding further.

I'd spoken to my boss and to Joanna. He had allowed me five days off in order to take Mildred home. Joanna was anxious that I wouldn't be able to get in touch with Baby. She was frightened for me. What would I do if Mildred became aggressive on the flight – or worse still, dropped dead?

I returned to the hospital again after work to find Mildred not sitting in the chair but in bed. I had with me a carton of cranberry juice and a gooseberry fool; her favourites. Steve the nurse told me an old friend of Mildred's from St. Mary's had been in to see her earlier. 'I'm sure she thought she was in the presence of God,' Steve told me. 'The friend is some sort of nun and came wearing all the get-up.'

Mildred was happy to see me. She had a little more gusto. 'That nun friend of mine, Sister Vilma, was here,' she said. 'She asked me if I wanna be buried in London or Los Angeles! Fuck!' she said, spluttering mousse over me and the bed. 'I told her I'm not going nowhere yet – like I need that kinda shit!' It continued to surprise me that, as someone so devout, Mildred was terrified of dying.

I was asked to remain with her as two neurological specialists chatted with her. Mildred suddenly became extremely lucid, listening carefully to what they had to say. She then asked the question: 'Can I go and see my Baby?'

She was planning for us to leave London for LA in ten days' time.

* * *

Kirsty agreed to help me with Mildred. We met outside Chelsea and Westminster at seven in the evening. Kirsty was shocked at Mildred's appearance, having seen her only a few days previously at the wedding.

I packed as Kirsty sat holding Mildred's hand. Mildred explained how Baby needed her mother and how, if Baby had married Prince Charles, she'd have without question remained in London and close to her Mama. Mildred didn't notice that Kirsty had tears in her eyes.

We both accompanied her down to the X-Ray department. An hour later, her surgeon, Dr Barrow, told us Mildred was fit to fly. The look on Kirsty's face said it all: *'How?'*

It was late by the time we got back to the flat. Mildred asked Kirsty to help her shower and wash her hair. Mildred couldn't have managed without her. Cutting her toenails was one thing, but washing Mildred? It was something I'd not signed up for. I could hear my mother – but Mildred was right: she needed full-time care now.

Mildred headed to bed just as Kirsty left. She invited Kirsty to a small birthday soirée she was planning to host the next Tuesday. When I checked in on Mildred just before eleven she was sitting up and writing invitations. She handed me the three she'd already penned to post. Each one was smudged and covered in lipstick-stained drool.

I'd read an article years ago written by someone who'd interviewed screen legend Bette Davis when she was age-withered and battling cancer and the effects of a stroke. It was entitled *Battling Bette*. Mildred was giving Bette a run for her money – falling apart yet planning a party and a transatlantic flight. I was secretly hoping the doctor would step in and order her to stay put.

* * *

Five days later I walked out of the office. I would not return for two weeks, and when I did I'd be a free man.

I'd sat with my boss for thirty minutes. He'd applauded my commitment to 'the Hollywood actress'. With Marigold thankfully away, Stefan sat in on our meeting. Tearful, I told them both that Mildred probably had just a couple of weeks left.

'I'll tell you something,' said my boss, his hand on my shoulder, 'you should write a book about your experiences one day.' He shook my hand, as did Stefan.

* * *

I went out early on the morning of Mildred's birthday to buy breakfast and gifts: fresh fruit, Danish pastries, eggs, spinach, and a bottle of Moët. The girl in the ladies' shoe department at the Army & Navy store on Victoria Street kindly wrapped my gift of a pair of dusty pink suede shoes.

She was up and about when I got back; she'd had a double dose of sleeping pills and two double vodka martinis the night before. 'I feel like I've been reborn,' she said.

I left her in the recliner watching television. Taking a leaf from Howard's book, I dressed the dining table with her best linen, silver, and Spode. I fixed breakfast and invited her to the table. It was only the fourth time we had ever sat and eaten together.

The buzzer went; it was a florist delivering flowers from Joanna and her parents – Mildred wept at their magnificence. I fetched the birthday cards that had been arriving all week, which I'd hidden in my room. I helped her to open them. They were from my parents, from Corinne, Maurus and Ingrid, Kirsty, and Joanna's grandparents. She gave each one a lipstick kiss, paying close attention to a card from Selene Walters, another from Shirley Chambers, and a scrawled message from Zsa Zsa Gabor.

After breakfast she spent the remainder of the morning floating around in her blue dressing gown, leaving behind her a soggy trail of tissues. At eleven, she asked that I fix her a vodka martini.

I suggested she rest before lunch, so that I could have

time to clear up the flat and make dozens of canapés. Guests were due from five-thirty.

The phone rang intermittently throughout the morning. The call she savoured most was from Dr Parsons, who'd instructed Nelly-Lyn to give Mildred a month's supply of medication for our impending trip. She came off the phone elated. Mildred was eager for me to go to the surgery post-haste in case 'the doc' should change his mind. When I arrived, the receptionist asked me to wait a moment. Doctor Parsons wanted to see me. Before handing over two carrier bags, he shook my hand warmly.

'Your dedication to Miss Shay should warrant you a Purple Heart,' he said. 'If only a quarter of my patients had someone like you.'

I couldn't help it; knowing that it would be the last time I visited the surgery, and her last birthday, the tears flowed. I wasn't quite sure if the doctor was prepared. I begged him to intervene and put a stop to Mildred's request to fly thousands of miles to see her daughter. He all but shrugged his shoulders. 'She's got some willpower – who am I to stop her?' he said.

'You're her doctor,' I argued.

He bade me farewell.

Friends from St. Mary's, Kiki, Rosemary, and Timothy, were the first to arrive, led by Father Cherry. Of the bevy of ladies, Jennifer Howarth was perhaps the most intriguing. Obsessed with cats, her coat was covered in cat hair, her eye make-up feline, and her handbag emblazoned with a giant Hello Kitty. When I asked how she was, Jennifer brushed her left ear with her cupped hand as she purred like Eartha Kitt as Catwoman. Her look couldn't have been more different, however – more like that of the grandmother in *Tweetie Pie* than the feline star. As Jennifer left, the Shermans arrived. Mr Sherman was in a red sequined fish-tail evening gown, his bald head a contrast to his hairy shoulders and back. Behind the Shermans, Sister Vilma entered with a superfluity of nuns.

The friends brought champagne with them and lavished her with gifts. The champagne bubbles triggered the hernia in her diaphragm, which caused her to burp constantly, but it didn't stop her recounting stories of her gilded life. Every so often she chewed on a Rennie, the result of which was a giant build-up of gas. Her voice became akin to Linda Blair in *The Exorcist*. I couldn't help but laugh as Mildred gave an unwittingly good performance.

Mildred kept the conversation clean while the nuns were there. After an hour Vilma and a nun named Maureen bade Mildred farewell – not before they'd cleared most the canapés, sausage rolls, and half a salmon quiche into Maureen's *Mary Poppins*-style carpet-bag, having complained to Mildred that the oven at the convent was on the blink and they'd got nothing for supper.

Feeling sorry for the sisters, Mildred begged them to take more. Happy to oblige, Vilma picked up the Rococo chocolates Kiki had bought Mildred and took a bottle of milk from the fridge. I relieved her of the chocolates just as the lift door closed.

Kirsty arrived much later, with a bouquet of gardenias to remind Mildred of her house in West Palm

Beach. Behind her came Adam and Lee with a bottle of dazzling nail varnish, and Corinne with food to replenish the depleted buffet and bottle of champagne.

After forty minutes, Mildred began to nod off. She was awake when Adam and Kirsty hugged her perhaps harder than ever before; Lee too, once he'd come out from the kitchen after a good cry. They knew, as did Corinne and Mildred's friends from St. Mary's, that they'd probably never see her again.

Father Cherry stayed long enough to offer Mildred Holy Communion.

Four days later, my alarm went off at five-thirty. Our flight left later that morning. I'd be back in just a matter of days, my life quite transformed.

Eighteeen

California

I looked over from the baggage carousel towards Mildred. She seemed so tiny sitting in an airport wheelchair. Her mink coat kept out the chill of the air-conditioning and her supersize sunglasses blocked the stares of curious travellers. Her head was slumped over to one side; her hair was still blonde, but thinning now; wispy tufts peeped out from under her Panama hat. Her lipstick was smudged across her face, disfigured so much now that it was reminiscent of Munch's *The Scream*.

I returned my gaze, concentrating on extracting our bags from the bustle of the carousel. I jostled between two large Californians on one side of me and a middle-aged woman to my right. With all seven of our bags and the battered Peter Jones hatbox accounted for, I heaved them onto the trolley I'd battled for previously and began to push it to where I'd left a wilted Mildred.

One of the burly Californians tapped me on the shoulder. 'Excuse me, sir. Your friend over there, I've been watching her. She's so glamorous. Is she anybody?' I was caught off-guard slightly; over the last few weeks, I hadn't thought of her as being glamorous at all.

I pulled the trolley to a halt. 'Yes, she was somebody.' Then I corrected myself: 'She is somebody – an old movie star. Her name is Mildred Shay. She began her career during the early thirties at MGM. She was a cowgirl too, in Westerns.'

The Californian repeated my every word to her tanned friend, who was half-listening as she rooted through her handbag.

'Darlene, you got a pen? I gotta get her autograph for Tray.' She looked at me. 'Tray's my son. He is twenty…I can't believe he is twenty!' She shook her head. 'Tray is an old movie nut. He works in a comic store while he's at college. Sometimes people bring in old magazines to sell; you know, those old-time movie ones. I bet your friend was on the cover of one? They're like, so old. What pictures was she in?'

I looked skywards as I scrabbled to recall. 'Er, *The Women*, *Balalaika*…She dubbed for Garbo in *Grand Hotel*…She knew Errol Flynn.' The woman continued to hang onto my every word, flapping her hand, trying to get Darlene's attention away from the mountain of luggage being churned onto the baggage carousel. I mentioned that Mildred had known Clark Gable and Alfred Hitchcock. Darlene finally located a pen in the bottom of an enormous Shaun the Sheep rucksack and immediately delved in again for something which Mildred could sign.

I glanced over to Mildred, still hiding behind her giant sunglasses. I knew she'd been watching. I gave her a wave. Mildred reciprocated. I smiled in return – there was a little life in her yet. There had been a time not so long ago when she'd have stood talking at the woman, and afterwards bitched about how deplorable she found their size and their touristy wardrobe.

She called for me. As I approached a long line of drool swung from her mouth, then broke and settled on the left lapel of her fur coat.

I bent down beside her. 'Orstin, are we in Hollywood?' she asked. I nodded.

Mildred kissed a St. Christopher on a chain around her neck. 'Oh, boy, I made it.'

She then spied the two Californians, who were hovering behind me hoping for an autograph. Like a scared child, she hid her face behind the collar of her mink. For the first time in the years I'd known Mildred, she seemed scared. Other passengers stared over at her; she was attracting attention like she'd always attracted attention, but this time her look was quite different from her days as Hollywood's Pocket Venus. I shouted in her ear: 'Mildred, they are fans. They would very much like your autograph.'

'Hey, miss,' said Darlene's friend as she loomed over us. 'Honey, my name is Misty. Can I have your autograph? Your friend tells me you were famous.'

Their attention and their pleas gave Mildred a sudden zap of energy. She peeled back her fur collar and flashed her one good eye. The false eyelashes on her left were still attached, like a lifeless spider squashed onto her cheek.

'Darlings,' she said, her voice barely audible, 'I still have an eye. The craziest thing happened. I got an infection and poked it with an artificial tear dropper. Isn't that crazy?'

This was Mildred's story for the facial disfigurement; everyone from Heathrow to LA had been fed the same line. Misty turned to me.

'Your friend is lovely, but honey,' she said, 'I can't

understand what she's a-sayin'.' Misty stared. 'I'm a nurse at Cedars-Sinai. She's pretty sick, ain't she?' I nodded. She rubbed my back sympathetically.

Misty knelt in front of Mildred. She didn't seem to react a bit to Mildred's spit as it landed on her. 'I was infamous, darling,' Mildred told her. Other inquisitive onlookers formed a circle around us.

'Who is she?' asked a British girl, probably twenty-five.

'She's a movie star,' I told her.

* * *

Mildred died a few days later in a Glendale hospital on October 15th, 2005. Staff said she'd been a fighter and had spoken constantly of 'my darling boys – my bricks'. A photo of Howard and me with Joanna and Mildred at the wedding stood proudly by her bed.

Her send-off was simple, or so I was told. It was made clear to me that I was not expected to attend. I hoped her ashes had been scattered close to her beloved Geoffrey.

Despite all the dramas, the tantrums, and the tribulations, I was proud of Mildred and I loved her. I instinctively knew that my life would never be the same again.

Mildred confided in me during our first encounter that she wanted to author a book, but couldn't knuckle down to write it because she talked too much. Well, Cissie, your words made *Pocket Venus: The Rise, Fall & The Rise of a Hollywood Starlet* possible, and the truth is my life would have been only half-lived had I not written it.

Acknowledgements

I would like to thank:

Mildred Shay, who I fondly called 'Cissie', for always talking and enabling me to write our story.

My wife Joanna for her unwavering support before, during and after the time we lived with 'Cissie'.

My twin brother Howard, for his edits on his morning and evening commute to Geneva. 'Never forget'.

Louise Naudé, a support, a voice of reason, a first rate editor.

Tom Perrin, for believing in 'Pocket Venus' and for your vision.

Carissa Fortino, for your wise words and friendship and for championing 'Pocket Venus'.

Susannah Bonsanquet for your support and friendship for believing in 'Pocket Venus'.

To John and Pamela, my parents, for your friendship towards Mildred and your love and support.

To Kenneth and Julie Gabb, my parents-in-law for your friendship towards Mildred and so much more.

To Resheda, Mildred's long-suffering 'Home Help'.

To Stephanie Seacombe and Martin McAngus, who

read my first draft a decade ago and who willed me to keep writing.

To Elena Hill and Charles Shearn, for your photography and Ben Glazier and the 'Creatives' at Glazier Design for design assistance.

To Michael Pick, Julian Fellowes, Rob Harris, Chris Weitz, Julia Robson, Frances Card, Andy Hall, Charlotte Metcalfe, Con & Tina Gornell and Sophie Winkleman for continuing to champion me.

There were many who enriched Mildred's life and mine during the time we were friends and who helped when she, Joanna and I need you most:

Kirsty Craik, Adam James (for your friendship and design skills), Corinne Manches, Ferhat Soygenis (for your help – I wish you'd known her), Jason & Rachael Meek, John Curran, Lady Janet Marchioness of Milford-Haven, Dr. Edward & Sally Henderson, Mr. Ali (Mr. Ali's Convenience Store, Ebury St.), Roy & Betty Barton, Lee Paton, Moira Gould, Claire Taylor, Barry & Rowena Beech, Viscount & Lady Davidson, Alan O'Sullivan, Shehnaz O'Mallie, Jon Moore, Christopher Sharples, Sara Vaughn, Eric Way, Alex Proud, Malcolm Spencer, Michelle Jones, Aisling Meek, Benjamin Meek, Suzanne Kaaren, Shirley Chambers, Zsa Zsa Gabor, Glenn Ford, Selene Walters Lamm, Elizabeth Taylor, June Epstein, Mildred's friends Tim, Kiki, Gerda, Rosemary, Jennifer, David & Victoria Foster, Father Cherry & all at St. Mary's Bourne Street, Diane Blake Ohman, Julie Meine, 'LA' Carole, Father John & Marjorie Farrant, the staff at The Cavalry & Guards Club, 127 Piccadilly, Dr. Barrow, professionals & volunteers at

Chelsea & Westminster Hospital, Doctor O'Brien & staff at Belgravia Surgery, staff at Belgravia Post Office, Larry, the Porter (Cundy Street Flats), Gordon Waller & finally to Ms. Georgina S. Waller, known to me as 'Baby'.

Every effort has been made to obtain permissions for the copyright materials, both illustrative and quoted. If there has been any omissions in this respect, the publishers and author offer their sincere regrets and will be pleased to ensure that an appropriate acknowledgement will appear in any future edition.